New Answers

to the

FATIGUE PROBLEM

New Answers

to the

FATIGUE PROBLEM

ADELAIDE K. BULLEN

(formerly of The Fatigue Laboratory, Harvard University)

UNIVERSITY OF FLORIDA PRESS

Gainesville

1956

To my mother

GRACE MARBLE KENDALL

PREFACE

BECAUSE MY PURPOSE IN WRITING THIS BOOK has been to bring a clear picture to a wide audience, I have intentionally avoided the use of technical terms. As I. A. Richards, coauthor of *The Meaning of Meaning,** once said, "It is the little words that mean the most—'to know,' 'to do,' 'to be.' " It is with these "little" words I hope to reach specialists of many fields and readers with many interests. Each one can then "translate" the ideas presented here into the familiar terminology of his own field.

I have also presented the material in a special order and a special way to give a rounded picture of what is happening. The laboratory tests, which were used as guides for the field work, appear at the end of the book after we have had a chance to describe different types of people and to see how things looked in real life situations. I have done this because it is easy to take out *one* aspect of a situation and measure it minutely. Often, however, it is not so easy to

*C. K. Ogden and I. A. Richards, Rev. Ed. (New York: Harcourt, Brace and Company, 1953).

see how test tube findings work out in the complex of life itself. To show how different factors influence each other and to give insight into some of the checks and balances of the real world, I have used a narrative style for the presentation of the field studies. Because this is "easy" reading, the reader should not fail to notice the implications of what is happening.

As this book presents the results of original research rather than a study of past writings on the subject, only key sources are noted where of particular interest. Two books by William H. Sheldon and his collaborators, *The Varieties of Human Physique* (Harper & Brothers, 1940) and *The Varieties of Temperament* (Harper & Brothers, 1942), have been a great stimulus to the present study. References to Sheldon's material on physique and temperament contained in this text will be found in these books. As this book was submitted to the publisher in 1954, literature after that is not covered here.

Documentation of laboratory methods, presentation of form sheets and questionnaires, discussion of field techniques—while extremely important at each stage of the research—could fill another book! As all pioneer work builds on the past but points to the future, the scope of this presentation invites new techniques and implementation from many fields rather than maintaining the vested interests of the past. I hope this book will be a springboard to greater understanding.

Here we look at the people themselves in three distinct situations— office, factory, and laboratory. Two forward-looking industrial concerns were chosen for these studies. Both companies have shown spectacular growth and continue to enlarge year by year. Their policy of ever looking for ways to improve, of hunting down their weak spots, may have contributed to this growth in no small measure.

The Textron study was made in one of Textron's former textile plants. The Filetab Company has preferred to have a fictitious name used. However, both companies, in paying for expenses incidental to the field work, intended not only to benefit themselves but to share their findings with industry as a whole. All workers contacted in connection with the research were told it was to help workers in general. Their sincerity and cooperation are greatly appreciated. Actual names of people and places have not been used.

Laboratory subjects at the Fatigue Laboratory, Graduate School of Business Administration, Harvard University, knew that publications would ultimately result from the research in which they participated. As in the industrial studies, individuals remain anonymous. Additional comparative data on these subjects was made available to us through the Harvard Hygiene Department, who in cooperation with the Grant Study had previously collected data on a number of the college men in our laboratory series.

Data on WACs and nurses included here were collected by the author in the capacity of Civilian Consultant to the War Department and have already appeared in a scientific article which had official army release. No new data are added; however I hope the WACs and Army Nurse Corps will benefit from seeing their data set beside civilian incidences.

I am indebted to many people and institutions for making possible the collection and analysis of the present material. I wish to express my gratitude to my many professors in the social sciences, particularly to the late Dr. Earnest A. Hooton, physical anthropologist of Harvard, and Dr. Clyde Kluckhohn, social anthropologist of Harvard, who gave me valuable training and encouragement. The field studies in industry benefited from the enthusiastic interest and help of the late Elton Mayo, Graduate School of Business Administration, Harvard. Dr. William H. Forbes, physiologist (now at the Harvard School of Public Health) formerly acting director of the Fatigue Laboratory, gave me wonderful opportunity in my job there—which was to initiate and direct research on nervous and mental fatigue. Dr. M. A. B. Brazier, director of the Electroencephalographic (Brain Wave) Laboratory, Massachusetts General Hospital, cooperated in tests by letting us use her laboratory and technicians. Dr. C. H. Sandage, now of the University of Illinois, gave expert help in the design of questionnaires. My loyal research assistant, Mary Jane Peck (now Mrs. Robert Meuleman), gave technical assistance of many kinds. Thanks would not be complete without mention of the Florida State Museum, where I am Associate in Anthropology and where I have carried out final analysis of the data, written technical papers, and written this book.

A. K. B.

Florida State Museum
Gainesville, Florida

CONTENTS

PART I - YOUR BODY TYPE

INTRODUCTION

I SUPPOSE WE ARE ALL PUZZLES TO OURSELVES, and I am sure we are to our friends, so it may be profitable to look at people as puzzles for a little while. We can break up the whole of our life into some of its parts and look at the pieces as we would at an unsolved jigsaw puzzle. When we put the parts together, we may see "the whole picture" in a new light; and, if we want to make some pieces fit together a little better, we may smooth a few rough edges here and there.

I shall first try to show you how to tell what kind of body you have (Part I), then how different types of people feel and behave in given work situations (an office, Part II—and a factory, Part III). Last of all, some findings from laboratory tests on nervous and mental fatigue will be mentioned in the light of what we found out in Parts I to III. By the time you get to Part V, I hope you can put your own puzzle together so that *you*—a real person in real life—emerge. If you have found how to fit the parts of your life together a little better, if one rough edge has been smoothed, this little book will be happy to have served you.

3

I. SEVEN SAMPLES

In DISCUSSING TYPES OF PEOPLE WITH YOU, I merely want to call your attention to kinds of people you already know. As we look at different characteristics and how they tend to occur together, you will say to yourself, "Why, I knew this all the time." And that is the truth.

The fact is that for the practical purposes of the business man, the personnel expert, the worker himself, and others interested in applying reliable knowledge, fine points become of academic interest only. Correlations that don't "hit you in the face" are too controversial to be widely applied.

For these reasons, I have found that putting people in seven major groups is reliable for practical applications and meaningful to correlate with psychological and social factors. In this presentation I shall try to develop useful ideas without splitting hairs or resorting to the jargon of the specialist. In talking *to* people *about* people, one can be very down-to-earth and straightforward. A mumbo jumbo of terms is no help and merely obscures the few useful ideas we all can put to work right now.

4

For instance, let's look at people for a minute as though they were shapes. Let's take a sphere, a cube, and a tall, narrow rectangular block (see Figure 1). You've known amiable, oval people (soft spheres!), hard-hitting square guys (big-boned, muscular cubes!), and sensitive, fragile fellows (delicate, linear slivers!). But you say, "Those are extremes. They are the exceptions." I agree.

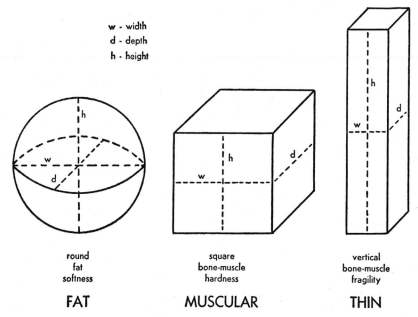

w - width
d - depth
h - height

round
fat
softness

FAT

square
bone-muscle
hardness

MUSCULAR

vertical
bone-muscle
fragility

THIN

Fig. 1 — People are SHAPES. Three basic tendencies.

Now let's look at a few combinations (see Figure 2). First, take a cube and overlay him with a soft, spherical padding of fat. Does he sound familiar? Then take a tall sliver and stretch him out a little in the direction of the cube. Know him? Then take your sliver and put a little plump padding on him. Yes, these make three more types. And you will learn to spot these three almost as

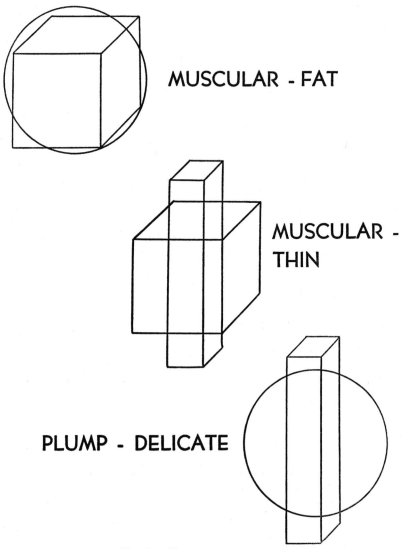

MUSCULAR - FAT

MUSCULAR - THIN

PLUMP - DELICATE

Fig. 2 — Three combinations

easily as you do your old friends, the extremes. However, you may still find many people who don't fit into any of the six groups.

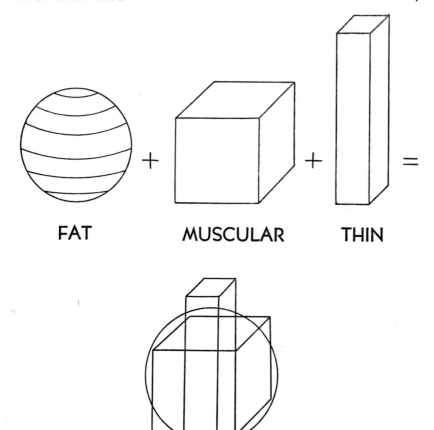

FAT + MUSCULAR + THIN =

MODERATE MIXTURE

Fig. 3 — THREE TENDENCIES COMBINED

For these average people, these middle-of-the-roaders, we have a convenient category (see Figure 3). They combine the three original tendencies with none to an extreme, or even very pronounced, degree. We call them MODERATE MIXTURES. You will find a little roundness here, a little fragility there, a little squareness somewhere else; or you will find that you can't decide about anything! It's all just in-between. All right. Stop worrying. Your worries are over. They are MODERATE MIXTURES and are a very common species. One tendency may be a bit more in evidence, but none is highly pronounced. They are average, they are combinations, they are regular fellows that come by the dozen.

For our own convenience, let's give the seven types simple names. Let's call the sphere FAT, the cube MUSCULAR, and the sliver THIN. Then for our three combination types we can say MUSCULAR-FAT, MUSCULAR-THIN, and PLUMP-DELICATE (the sliver with a little fat). As noted above, MODERATE MIXTURES take care of the rest.

Obviously the three combination types (MUSCULAR-FAT, MUS-CULAR-THIN, and PLUMP-DELICATE) combine definite characteristics of the two types of which they are composed, or the results will show a blend of the two tendencies with a balance of influences. The MODERATE MIXTURES similarly blend all *three* tendencies with none pronounced, although sometimes they will show observably distinct features of different kinds in different parts of their anatomies with no dominant picture of one or two trends.

Also, you will notice that when you have two trends predominant, they are rarely exactly equal. Sometimes one and sometimes the other is present to a higher degree. Therefore one might say a MUSCULAR-*FAT man* when fat was more pronounced or a FAT-*MUSCULAR man* when bone and muscle were more pronounced. Likewise, there might be distinguished a MUSCULAR-*THIN man* when sliver tendencies were more pronounced and a THIN-*MUS-CULAR man* when bone and muscle were more in evidence. It will be noticed that very frequently women are MUSCULAR-*FAT* or MUSCULAR-*THIN,* whereas men are very often FAT-*MUSCULAR* or THIN-*MUSCULAR.* However, as these are all instances of the combination of two dominant trends, social and psychological correlations of the present study need not stress finer distinctions as to degree of predominance.

DO THESE FORMS MAKE MATHEMATICAL SENSE?

When you get used to checking different people, you will find that there are common combinations of features. You will begin to look at people as *wholes*. And when you do, you will see that something is happening—as D'Arcy Thompson[1] points out—to the organism as a unit.

Look at the outlines (Figure 4). The FAT person is blown out in the middle: this concentrates his mass in such a way that small hands and feet and tapering arms and legs are a part of the whole picture. His head repeats the sphere; his cheeks may be blown out. Similarly you will notice that the MUSCULAR man in his cubic way has no centralization but seems to be rugged on the corners. His hands and feet are heavy and massive, his shoulders square out as opposed to the sloping shoulders of the FAT man. His head is cubical and heavy. And lastly, the THIN person looks merely vertical: he is not spherical, he is not cubical. Nothing is softened (rounded) or strengthened (squared). His bony structure is light. His arms and legs are linear and delicate as compared to those of FAT and MUSCULAR. His hands tend to be long and slender. It is easy to see how each part of the body fits into the picture of each body as a whole.

Moreover, combination tendencies of two groups of traits (MUSCULAR-FAT, MUSCULAR-THIN, PLUMP-DELICATE) make sense as they combine two trends. The individual is not a meaningless conglomeration of accidentally arranged parts. In a recent article[2] I have shown how measurements of the seven types I have outlined have average measurements that fall in a definite sequence. Also the proportions of various parts of the body reflect the relationship of the major pattern. Ratio of height to width tends to show a consistent picture

[1] *On Growth and Form,* New Ed. (Cambridge, England: Cambridge University, 1942).
[2] A. K. Bullen, "Qualitative and Quantitative Theory as Applied to Body Build Research," *The Quarterly Journal of the Florida Academy of Sciences,* XVI, 1 (1953), 35-64.

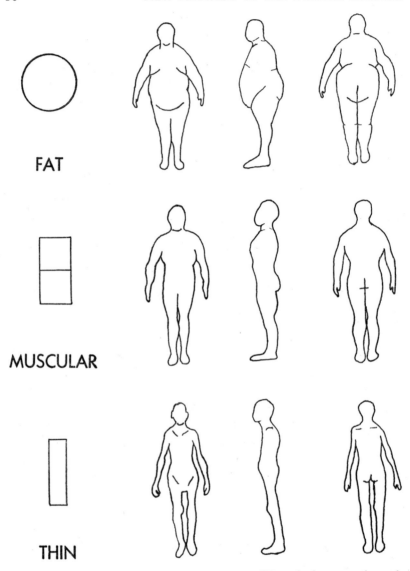

FAT

MUSCULAR

THIN

Fig. 4 — OUTLINES OF PEOPLE AND SHAPES. (Three basic types of people outlined from Sheldon's original examples, in W. H. Sheldon, S. S. Stevens, and W. B. Tucker, *The Varieties of Human Physique*, 1940, Harper & Brothers.)

throughout the body: for instance, length and width of hands and feet are apt to correspond to the basic relationship of height and weight (width trend).

We see that each body expresses a basic idea. D'Arcy Thompson would say it is a resultant of forces; Aristotle would say it displays "the more" and "the less"—"excess" and "defect"—as compared to the basic form; and Plato would suggest it corresponds more or less to the type itself—to *the IDEA of a man*. William H. Sheldon considers the ideal idea the perfectly balanced MODERATE MIXTURE with each of the three major tendencies midway between lack and extreme. However, we may rightly ask whether there may not be the "idea" of specialized types as well as of the balanced form. The ideal for different purposes may find expression in the ideals of differing types. Our job is to know what these types are and to try to grasp the meaning of these forms in action. We will have to let the philosophers argue as to whether different types were created for different purposes. We can work on an everyday level and ask:

Where are these forms found?

2. TYPES WE FIND

In women at work

For a bird's-eye view of some women at work, let's look at the distribution of types of women found in the groups of factory workers, office workers, WACs, and nurses who were studied on the job.[3] You will notice (Table 1) that about a third of all the women are MODERATE MIXTURES. Of the remaining six types, three—THINS, FATS, and MUSCULAR-FATS—are relatively common (roughly 10 to 20 per cent) and three—MUSCULARS, MUSCULAR-THINS, and PLUMP-DELICATES—are relatively rare (under 10 per cent).

In 4,012 males

Although ratings on a student group are not directly comparable to the present findings for workers, it is of interest to see how types may cluster in a large group of males. Table 2 shows relatively few FATS and THINS as compared with the women, while the

[3]In the present work, all data on WACs and nurses comes from the article cited in footnote 2, page 9.

TABLE 1

727 WOMEN
(547 Army Nurse and WAC, 130 Office, and 50 Factory)

FAT	-------17%-------
MUSCULAR-FAT	----11%----
MUSCULAR	--6%--
MUSCULAR-THIN	--5%-
THIN	---------21%---------
PLUMP-DELICATE	-4%-
MODERATE MIXTURE	----------------35%----------------

MUSCULARS and MUSCULAR-THINS are two and three times as common as among women workers. MUSCULAR-FATS and MODERATE MIXTURES are about equal for both groups.

TABLE 2

4,012 MALE COLLEGE STUDENTS*

FAT	-4%-
MUSCULAR-FAT	-----13%-----
MUSCULAR	----11%----
MUSCULAR-THIN	-------16%------
THIN	---9.5%---
PLUMP-DELICATE	---7%--
MODERATE MIXTURE	------------------39.5%-----------------

*Arranged into seven groups from Sheldon's original list of male somatotypes (Sheldon, Stevens, and Tucker, *The Varieties of Human Physique*).

In a few men at work

When we look at the distribution of body types in a group of twenty-one men in an office of whom one-third were hired primarily to lift sixty-pound file cabinets, we are not surprised to find (Table 3) that they are high in occurrence of MUSCULAR men as compared with both the average for women's groups and for male students. The majority of the boys who lift files are MUSCULAR. However, when they are subtracted from the total twenty-one, MUSCULAR men in the office become about equal to an average incidence for

TABLE 3

SOME COMPARISONS

	WOMEN 727	MALE STUDENTS 4,012	OFFICE MEN 21	OFFICE MEN Excluding heavy files	Heavy files* 7
FAT	17%	4%	5%	7%	0%
MUSCULAR-FAT	11%	13%	14%	21%	0%
MUSCULAR	6%	11%	24%	7%	57%
MUSCULAR-THIN	5%	16%	5%	0%	14%
THIN	21%	9.5%	10%	7%	14%
PLUMP-DELICATE	4%	7%	0%	0%	0%
MODERATE MIXTURE	35%	39.5%	43%	57%	14%

*See discussion of Collating Section, "Office Workers," Part II.

women (see Table 3). The office distribution for men—with or without the file boys—shows no PLUMP-DELICATES and fewer FATS and THINS than the women.

It is clear from the first three tables that there is an overlapping of types among men and women, but that the distribution of types squares with common knowledge. That is, in general men tend to have a bigger bony framework and larger muscles than women, whereas women are more apt to be delicate and soft. This does not mean that some women are not larger and stronger than some men or that small-boned, weak-muscled men do not exist. It does mean that we can expect to find more muscular men than muscular women.

Also, as we pointed out on page 8, combination muscular types will tend to show more men who are predominantly MUSCULAR with FAT or THIN tendencies in second place, whereas women will be more apt to be FAT or THIN predominantly with a secondary emphasis on MUSCULAR development. In extreme development of bone and muscle, men will tend to show examples which exceed muscular development in any normal woman. When a woman is as muscular as an average man, she appears to be a decidedly muscular woman.

In assessing men and women in relation to their job potential, it is important to bear in mind the whole range of strength and delicacy which occurs among both men and women so that strong thin men will not fall into the same category with delicate women. Also, strong women may handle many physical jobs but should not be expected to qualify for the same physical jobs that extremely muscular men can handle. As borne out in common practice, where extreme physical strength is required, requisite power will be found among extremely developed strong men.

In appraising body type for both men and women, it is important not to confuse FAT people with *MUSCULAR*-FAT ones. Where muscular support is virtually lacking, many jobs that could be handled competently by a *strong* fat person are out of the question. One should be careful not to assign men to the purely FAT category when, in fact, they are MUSCULAR-FAT. While they may appear very fat when compared with highly developed MUSCULAR men, they are far from being in the class with predominantly FAT women of negligible muscular development. A majority of these men should fall into the MUSCULAR-FAT category found rather frequently in both men and women.

Research which includes job analysis and the basic requirements of a given job—*whether it is to be done by a man or a woman*—highlights the necessity for clear expression of absolute emphasis in physique regardless of the sex of the individual. For purposes of job placement, particularly in times of emergency and labor shortage, the question is: *What kind of person can do this job?*

It is to this question that we now address ourselves and look to see in what jobs and where in the population we find our seven kinds of people. Many studies will be needed to complete this survey and we hope others will carry on where this little book leaves off. Let's make a start and see where the seven types occur among some groups of women workers.

The following seven tables show the relative incidences of the seven types of body build among different groups of women: factory workers, statistical office workers, nurses, and WACs. Distributions of body type also include breakdowns as to civilian jobs held by

WACs and Army Nurses before they joined the services. Also breakdown by age and racial groups has been made as well as by regions of the country from which the women originally came. These pilot findings, while in some instances small in number, are presented here as suggestive of areas for future study. After you have looked over this initial series of tables to see where high and

TABLE 4

WHERE DO WE FIND FATS?*

Russian Women (of 19)	------------------37%-----------------	
Factory Workers (of 50)	------------26%-----------	
Office Workers (of 130)	-----------25%-----------	MANY
South Atlantic (of 39)	--------18%-------	
Total Women (of 727)	****17%****†	AVERAGE
Middle Atlantic (of 190)	-------17%-------	
‡Civilian Factory (of 36)	-------17%-------	
Civilian Nurses (of 289)	-------16%------	
Army Nurses (of 268)	-------16%------	
Civilian Office (of 83)	-------16%------	
Army Clerical Worker (of 54)	------15%------	
Negroid (of 27)	------15%------	
Women 35 and Under (of 466)	------14%-----	
WAC Enlisted (of 221)	------14%-----	
White (of 518)	------14%-----	
Women Over 35 (of 81)	------14%-----	
Civilian Teachers (of 23)	----9%---	
East North Central (of 49)	---8%---	
Balto-Ugric-Slav (of 25)	---8%---	FEW
Civilian Students (of 40)	--7.5%--	
WAC Officers (of 58)	--5%-	

*These FATS are not the most extreme of their type. Almost all have noticeable muscular support, even though this is negligible in amount when compared to men or women who fall into the MUSCULAR-FAT category. As all these women are active and have jobs, we realize they have greater muscle tone than FAT sedentary nonworkers.

†In this and similar tables, the percentage that appears in the row of asterisks represents the percentage in the total group; it is emphasized for ease in locating which groups fall above and below the average.

‡The term civilian as used here refers to the jobs held by Army Nurses and WACs before they joined the service.

low occurrences of particular types appear, you will see that—as for boys lifting file cabinets—a certain "sense" emerges from the assortment of distributions. For instance,

where do we find FATS?

You notice that FAT women have medium and high occurrence for office workers and are highest among factory workers and the few Russian women available for this study (Table 4).

Teachers, students, and WAC officers show few FAT women.

Civilian factory (22 per cent) and factory (16 per cent) workers are both high, over average, in MUSCULAR-FATS (Table 5).

TABLE 5

WHERE DO WE FIND MUSCULAR-FATS?

Civilian Factory (of 36)	----------22%---------	
West North Central (of 23)	----------22%---------	**MANY**
Civilian Teachers (of 23)	----------22%---------	
Russian Women (of 19)	---------21%---------	
Army Medical Technicians (of 107)	---------21%---------	
British Women (of 30)	-------17%-------	
WAC Enlisted (of 221)	-------16%------	
Factory (of 50)	-------16%------	
Women Over 35 (of 81)	------15%------	
Civilian Office (of 83)	------14%-----	
East North Central (of 49)	------14%-----	
Old American (of 272)	-----12%----	
New England (of 171)	-----12%----	
Total Women (of 727)	***11%**	**AVERAGE**
White (of 518)	----11%----	
Negroid (of 27)	----11%----	
Women 35 and Under (of 466)	---10.5%---	
Middle Atlantic (of 190)	---10.5%---	
Office Workers (of 130)	----10%---	
Civilian Nurse (of 289)	----9%---	
Army Nurse (of 268)	----9%---	
Balto-Ugric-Slav (of 25)	-4%-	
WAC Officers (of 58)	-3%	**FEW**
Civilian Students (of 40)	2.5%	
Civilian Physical Education Teachers (of 11)	0	

Civilian students and WAC officers are low in MUSCULAR-FATS.

Note that the percentage for the total group (11 per cent) is not far from the incidence for office workers (10 per cent) and nurses (9 per cent).

In general, MUSCULAR women are rare with most groups showing an incidence near the 6 per cent average for the total 727 (Table 6).

However, MUSCULARS are relatively high in the small group of civilian physical education teachers, among the physiotherapists, the WAC officers, and the Negroid and Russian women.

TABLE 6

WHERE DO WE FIND MUSCULARS?

Civilian Physical Education Teachers (of 11)	--------18%-------	
West North Central (of 23)	-------17%-------	MANY
Negroid (of 27)	------15%------	
WAC Officers (of 58)	-----12%----	
Army Physiotherapists (of 59)	-----12%----	
Russian Women (of 19)	---10.5%---	
South Atlantic (of 39)	----10%---	
Women Over 35 (of 81)	----9%---	
Civilian Office (of 83)	---7%--	
New England (of 171)	---7%--	
WAC Enlisted (of 221)	---7%--	
Women 35 and Under (of 466)	---7%--	
British Women (of 30)	---7%--	
White (of 518)	---7%--	
Civilian Nurse (of 289)	---7%--	
Army Medical Technician (of 107)	--6.5%-	
East North Central (of 49)	--6%--	
Total Women (of 727)	*6%*	AVERAGE
Army Nurse (of 268)	--6%--	
Old American (of 272)	--6%--	
Civilian Factory (of 36)	-5.5%-	
Office Workers (of 130)	--5%-	
Middle Atlantic (of 190)	--5%-	
Civilian Teachers (of 23)	-4%-	
Factory (of 50)	-4%-	FEW
Balto-Ugric-Slav (of 25)	-4%-	
Civilian Students (of 40)	2.5%	

Civilian students show fewest MUSCULARS.

As with the MUSCULAR type, MUSCULAR-THINS are relatively rare in most of these groups. The small civilian physical education teachers group again shows greatest incidence. WAC officers and civilian students show twice as high occurrence as the average.

Factory workers (both active and former civilian) are low in MUSCULAR-THINS. You will note that three groups have *no* MUSCULAR-THINS (civilian factory, Negroid, and Russian women).

Civilian students are highest in THINS (Table 8).

TABLE 7

WHERE DO WE FIND MUSCULAR-THINS?

Civilian Physical Education Teachers (of 11)	--------18%-------	
Balto-Ugric-Slav (of 25)	-----12%----	MANY
WAC Officers (of 58)	----10%---	
Civilian Students (of 40)	----10%---	
British Women (of 30)	----10%---	
Army Clerical Worker (of 54)	----9%---	
Women Over 35 (of 81)	----9%---	
Civilian Office Worker (of 83)	---8%---	
East North Central (of 49)	---8%---	
Army Medical Technician (of 107)	--7.5%--	
Office Workers (of 130)	--6%--	
WAC Enlisted (of 221)	--6%--	
White (of 518)	--6%--	
Old American (of 272)	-5.5%-	
Middle Atlantic (of 190)	--5%-	
Army Physiotherapist (of 59)	--5%-	
Total Women (of 727)	*5%*	AVERAGE
Women 35 and Under (of 466)	--5%-	
Civilian Teacher (of 23)	-4%-	
West North Central (of 23)	-4%-	
Civilian Nurse (of 289)	-4%-	
New England (of 171)	3.5%	
Army Nurse (of 268)	-3%	
South Atlantic (of 39)	-3%	
Factory (of 50)	2%	
Civilian Factory (of 36)	0	FEW
Negroid (of 27)	0	
Russian Women (of 19)	0	

Factory workers are next to the lowest.

Nurses and office workers are average.

There is a clear age factor evident in the occurrence of THIN women. Women 35 years old and under are high in THIN women, while women over 35 years old are low in incidence of THIN women.

It will be noticed that there are *no* THIN Russian women in the present series.

PLUMP-DELICATE women are extremely rare in all but a few groups, and nowhere are there more than 10 per cent in any group.

TABLE 8

WHERE DO WE FIND THINS?*

Civilian Students (of 40)	-----------------------55.5%-----------------------	
Negroid (of 27)	-----------------37%-----------------	
South Atlantic (of 39)	--------------31%--------------	
Army Clerical Worker (of 54)	-------------30%-------------	MANY
WAC Officers (of 58)	------------28%------------	
Army Physiotherapist (of 59)	-----------27%------------	
Old American (of 272)	----------24%----------	
Women 35 and Under (of 466)	----------24%----------	
East North Central (of 49)	----------22%----------	
WAC Enlisted (of 221)	----------22%----------	
Army Nurse (of 268)	----------22%----------	
White (of 518)	----------22%----------	
Middle Atlantic (of 190)	----------22%----------	
New England (of 171)	---------21%---------	
Total Women (of 727)	*****21%*****	AVERAGE
Civilian Nurse (of 289)	---------20%--------	
Office Workers (of 130)	---------20%--------	
Balto-Ugric-Slav (of 25)	---------20%--------	
Army Medical Technician (of 107)	---------20%--------	
Women Over 35 (of 81)	------15%------	
British Women (of 30)	-----13%-----	
West North Central (of 23)	----9%---	FEW
Factory (of 50)	---8%---	
Russian Women (of 19)	0	

*As noted for FAT women (footnote, Table 4), these THIN women show a little muscular development. Also some have slight evidence of plumpness in certain areas. None are the *extreme* of fragility.

Southern women, women over 35 years old, and civilian teachers show the highest incidence (Table 9).

Both the office and army clerical workers are low in PLUMP-DELICATE women. Four groups show *no* PLUMP-DELICATES (including physical education teachers and Negroid and Russian women).

MODERATE MIXTURES are common in all groups, with none having less than 20 per cent (Table 10).

Both army and civilian nurses, factory workers, and WAC officers are high in MODERATE MIXTURES.

TABLE 9

WHERE DO WE FIND PLUMP-DELICATES?

South Atlantic (of 39)	----10%---	
Civilian Teachers (of 23)	----9%---	
Women Over 35 (of 81)	----9%---	MANY
British Women (of 30)	---7%--	
Civilian Factory (of 36)	-5.5%-	
Army Medical Technician (of 107)	--5%-	
Old Americans (of 272)	--5%-	
Army Nurse (of 268)	-4.5%	
White (of 518)	-4%-	
Middle Atlantic (of 190)	-4%-	
Civilian Nurse (of 289)	-4%-	
New England (of 171)	-4%-	
East North Central (of 49)	-4%-	
Total Women (of 727)	*4%*	AVERAGE
Factory (of 50)	-4%-	
Balto-Ugric-Slav (of 25)	-4%-	
Civilian Office (of 83)	-4%-	
WAC Enlisted (of 221)	-4%-	
WAC Officers (of 58)	-3%	
Women 35 and Under (of 466)	-3%	
Civilian Student (of 40)	2.5%	
Office Workers (of 130)	2%	
Army Clerical Workers (of 54)	2%	
Army Physiotherapists (of 59)	2%	
West North Central (of 23)	0	FEW
Civilian Physical Education Teachers (of 11)	0	
Negroid (of 27)	0	
Russian Women (of 19)	0	

All office workers (office, civilian, and army clerical) are low average or low in MODERATE MIXTURES.

Civilian students are lowest in MODERATE MIXTURES.

TABLE 10

WHERE DO WE FIND MODERATE MIXTURES?

Balto-Ugric-Slav (of 25)	----------------------48%----------------------	
Army Nurses (of 268)	------------------40%------------------	
Factory (of 50)	------------------40%------------------	
Civilian Nurses (of 289)	------------------39.5%------------------	MANY
New England (of 171)	------------------39%------------------	
WAC Officers (of 58)	------------------38%------------------	
White (of 518)	----------------37%----------------	
Women 35 and Under (of 466)	----------------37%----------------	
Middle Atlantic (of 190)	----------------37%----------------	
British Women (of 30)	----------------37%----------------	
East North Central (of 49)	----------------37%----------------	
Civilian Physical Education Teachers (of 11)	----------------36%----------------	
Army Physiotherapist (of 59)	----------------36%----------------	
Total Women (of 727)	*********35%*********	AVERAGE
Civilian Teacher (of 23)	----------------35%----------------	
West North Central (of 23)	----------------35%----------------	
Old American (of 272)	---------------34%---------------	
Civilian Office (of 83)	---------------34%---------------	
Civilian Factory (of 36)	--------------33%--------------	
Russian Women (of 19)	--------------32%--------------	
Women Over 35 (of 81)	-------------31%-------------	
WAC Enlisted (of 221)	-------------31%-------------	
Office Workers (of 130)	-------------31%-------------	
Army Clerical (of 54)	-----------26%-----------	
Negroid (of 27)	----------22%---------	
South Atlantic (of 39)	--------20.5%--------	FEW
Civilian Student (of 40)	---------20%--------	

Now that we have some idea of different body types and how they occur in several groups, we may ask:

WHAT DO THESE DIFFERENCES MEAN?

Men's groups show a different emphasis from women's groups (Table 3). Women's groups show some common trends, but also show some groups which appear widely divergent from the average.

For instance, if we compare distribution for nurses, office workers, factory workers, and WAC officers with the average for the 727 women (Table 11), we find that nurses and office workers are much nearer the average distribution than the WAC officers and factory workers. Also, WAC officers and factory workers (except for mutually common MODERATE MIXTURES and rare PLUMP-DELI-CATES) veer in opposite directions. The two types—FAT and MUS-CULAR-FAT—that are *high* in factory are *low* in WAC officers. The three types—MUSCULAR, MUSCULAR-THIN, and THIN—that are *high* in WAC officers are *low* in factory.

TABLE 11

SOME VOCATIONAL COMPARISONS

	TOTAL WOMEN 727	WOMEN FACTORY 50	WOMEN OFFICE WORKERS 130	ARMY NURSE 268	WAC ENLISTED 221	WAC OFFICER 58
FAT	17%	26%	25%	16%	14%	5%
MUSCULAR-FAT	11%	16%	10%	9%	16%	3%
MUSCULAR	6%	4%	5%	6%	7%	12%
MUSCULAR-THIN	5%	2%	6%	3%	6%	10%
THIN	21%	8%	20%	22%	22%	28%
PLUMP-DELICATE	4%	4%	2%	4.5%	4%	3%
MODERATE MIXTURE	35%	40%	31%	40%	31%	38%

What do these variations mean? Do they mean that almost any woman can be a successful nurse or office worker, but that some women are less suited to be WAC officers or factory workers? Does it mean that the range of jobs for nurses and for office workers varies sufficiently to accommodate the varied qualities of many types, and that WAC officers and factory workers do more specialized kinds of work? What jobs do certain people prefer? Are these the people who do the job best? Are they likely to be "the chosen ones"?

To give well-considered explanations, we must know much more about the people on the job itself. It is not enough to look at distributions and make surmises. We must know more about how the people perform their jobs, about what their feelings are: whether they feel satisfaction or dissatisfaction in their work, whether they are tired out or just normally fatigued at the end of the day, whether they feel fine on one kind of job and "rotten" on another.

Let us go now to the office and factory (Parts II and III) and later to the controlled studies of the laboratory (Part IV) to become better acquainted with our seven types of people so that we can understand their feelings and know whether they are doing the work for which they are suited—to know more about what these distributions of human types mean.

PART II - IN AN OFFICE

INTRODUCTION

IT IS ONLY NATURAL for the reader to ask how the seven types of people described in Part I behave. Are they really different kinds of actors and reactors? Dr. Gordon W. Allport, psychologist, remarks in relation to this problem that Sheldon's book on *Varieties of Human Temperament* "alleviates our ignorance but at the same time makes us aware of the long road of research that lies ahead."

Yes, there is far to go before we understand the full meaning of human behavior—before we understand "why people do what they do" and also why a particular person does what he does when he does it. Therefore, let's work with a few people doing statistical office work. Let's look around and listen to what different people say. How *do* they act? What reactions do they *all* show? What reactions vary between people and groups? Is the reaction due to the situation or the person? Which factors are at work and how may they combine to create a given result?

3. I Work in an OFFICE

WHEN I WENT TO BEGIN STATISTICAL WORK in the Backs-to-Fronts
section of the Filetab Company's Checking Department, I didn't
realize that I was in the midst of the department's "middle-class"
workers. Below them in prestige were the lowly Transfer beginners
who merely copied figures all day long, while ahead of them in
Deals were the best workers promoted from Backs. Of the other
three sections, Signs was on a level with middle-class Backs, while
two were, as a worker told me, "separate"—Comptometer and
Collating.

I had explained the study to all the section supervisors at a special
meeting, so the woman in charge of Backs greeted me pleasantly
when I arrived the first morning. She understood my mission and
had told the workers about it. They knew I had been doing research
on ways to reduce nervous and mental fatigue and at present was
particularly interested in the effects of their newly installed musical
program.

She led me to a seat by the window and said, "It's nice out."
It was the last day of May and the view of grass and backyard

gardens was a cheerful sight. The Filetab Company had consciously chosen to locate itself on the edge of the city to attract desirable workers and have sufficient area for expansion. Workers appreciated, as I did, the fact that they were in the suburbs. They were glad not to have to commute to the downtown area or wear "city clothes" to work.

Before the supervisor left, she showed me how to do "backs-to-fronts." "There's very little comp work," she said. "Carrying the figuring from the back of the sheets to the front is similar most of the time, but there are little 'quirks' to different products. For instance, in syrups you have to make conversion from avoirdupois to ounces."

I settled down to work on the sheets. The work atmosphere made me feel comfortable and, to tell you the truth, rather proud of myself. It was fun to be part of such an attractive setting. The brick building was modern and gave an impression of restrained luxury as one entered it.

The fourth floor where I was working was light from the combined effect of ample windows, adequate illumination, and light-colored floors. The color scheme refreshed me. Venetian blinds in shades of green went with the pistachio walls. The ivory-colored ceiling was of perforated metal and did a fine job of deadening clicks and voice sounds.

I felt physically comfortable too. Ventilation and heating were good and the building was air-conditioned. Adequate work space avoided any crowded, huddled effect. Desks and chairs were of standard office types although the company hoped sometime to have adjustable office furniture of functional design.

I had gotten used to my surroundings and to the figuring by the time fifteen minutes of music came on at 9:45. The THIN girl near me alternately hummed and whistled "None but the Lonely Heart" as it came over. Although war in Europe had just ended (May, 1945), fighting was still going on with Japan, and I thought longing from war loneliness might be heightened for some workers by this selection. Especially in wartime any musical effect of sadness or longing should be avoided, it seemed to me. Once in a while a muted trumpet would blare out in a particularly loud and mournful way.

I had to count six as I used the comptometer and a jerky folk tune almost upset my count. The THIN girl commented that she liked violin solos if they were excellent and *not draggy*. A MUSCULAR-FAT woman said she liked piano and organ. My work neighbors were all friendly and eager to give me their reactions to the music. There was no rule about *not* talking. However, it was quite notice-able during the morning that workers tended to work during the playing and talk, not only to me, but with other groups in the room, at times when the music was off.

At quarter of eleven, THIN, MUSCULAR-FAT, and several other women asked me to go up with them to the lounge for a rest period. One said, "When you work with figures all day, you're glad to get away from them." They said it was all right for workers to use the elevator, so we rode up to the top floor where I found a cafeteria and large sitting room. You could get milk, cokes, nuts, and candies from vending machines. We stocked up and then sank into com-fortable chairs with soft seats and backs. End tables with ash trays were at our elbows and we were set for a pleasant chat.

Most of the people around us were eating and visiting in little groups like ours, but some women were reading, knitting, or writing letters. With the lounge and cafeteria completely set apart from the work situation, you really relaxed and felt in a different world. People could come up for fifteen minutes in small groups of their own choosing whenever they wanted to, *except* for the *Transfer* beginners. They all had to come at a set time.

Taking rest periods was an accepted practice in all sections. I noticed the day before when the manager telephoned one section, he asked, "Is so-and-so there or out at rest period?" There was no feeling that workers were exercising undue rights whenever they walked out for the fifteen minutes.

We had time for a leisurely little visit. We talked a bit about the music. One older woman with white hair said she didn't like to have it during particularly busy periods when she was trying to "get out the work." A young MODERATE MIXTURE who was going into the Marines said, "What I'm going to miss is the music."

While workers' comments about the music sound trivial, they had great significance for the whole research, as I could tie them in with reactions of different kinds of people to the same laboratory tests. The introduction of music created an experimental situation in the office. Of course, comments about other matters were also of interest.

For instance, after we got back to work again, MUSCULAR-FAT remarked that she liked the lounge but wished the company would also bring around orange juice at 10:30. She'd really like a lunch brought both in the middle of the morning and afternoon. "All of us are *hungry* at 11:45. We ate fairly early," she explained. Apparently for MUSCULAR-FAT the 10:45 snack in the lounge was insufficient. Most of the full-time office workers, however, felt there was ample access to food.

The supervisor of Backs asked me to eat lunch with her. Inexpensive meals were served in the cafeteria on the top floor. I really began to look forward to the break for lunch. The monotony of doing "backs-to-fronts" was beginning to "get" me. I had learned the procedure and now it was just repetition. Like most of the workers, I didn't really understand the logic of the figures. As the manager had told me, the "backs-to-fronts" process required logic to see that the totals fitted into the picture. But if the company hired people with that amount of judgment and logical turn of mind, they'd get bored by the routine handling of papers.

However, some workers like my smart neighbor THIN had acquired familiarity and skill. She said to me, "It makes you feel good to know as much about a product as anybody knows! They try to keep you on the same product each month as far as possible. You change during the month but are usually several days on each product." She used her head and really knew what the numbers meant for the different stores.

By twelve o'clock I got bored just copying figures I didn't understand and found myself gazing out the window and daydreaming. I noticed my workmate MUSCULAR-FAT hail a friend who was passing. The friend stopped and MUSCULAR-FAT engaged her in quite a long conversation. THIN also felt like diversion and was talking to the girl in front of her. I thought to myself, "I'd *give anything* to have some music." When the noontime program started at 12:30, workers made comments like: "Oh, goody, here it comes," and "This is good." I heartily agreed.

The girls lined up to punch the time clock before going for lunch at quarter of one. Backs had the latest of the staggered lunch periods. (Later the company rotated the order of lunch times so that no one section would always be early or late.) Music on the three-quarter-hour lunch program was still playing. MUSCULAR-FAT complained that there had been *too much violin.* My friends had heard the supervisor invite me for lunch and one of them said, "You're going with Lorna, aren't you?"

I was afraid they might resent my deserting them, but when I had lunch with the Backs workers on a following day, they showed great enthusiasm for supervision in general and for their supervisor in particular. THIN said, "She's about the sweetest person I ever knew. Do you notice how she's *last* in line every time we check out? She's *one of us.* She always understands about your little personal troubles. She knows when you have an 'off' day. She'll say, 'Oh, we all have off days when you just can't get out production.' The other supervisors are nice too. . . . Everyone is nice here. When you first come, you feel right at home. Nobody snubs you because you're new. Everyone is so pleasant."

At lunch Lorna showed her sympathy with the workers. She said gently, "It's hard to be *tied to a desk.*" Although she moved about, she had previously done desk work and knew what it meant. I could see why workers liked her. She was kind and understood the job. "If a girl is tired," she said, "she slows down, looks away, stalls. The monotony of the job would drive some people crazy."

THIN sat near us at lunch and made several comments about her reaction to the work. The way she showed fatigue, she said, was: "My *back gets tired* and I feel light in my stomach. . . . I feel as though I'd done a week's work when I work under pressure to get out an order by five o'clock." Later she suggested, "Rubber cushions for the seats would *help*." Although most workers appeared not to mind the hardness, I noticed next day that two THINS in the Deals section had gotten rubber cushions for the seats of their chairs. Apparently THIN's suggestion was particularly pertinent for THIN people.

After we had finished eating, we sat and talked for a while. We didn't feel hurried as the forty-five-minute lunch period wasn't over. When it was time, we took the elevator back down to the Checking Department floor. I took leave of my friends from Backs and went to another section of the large workroom where the Transfer beginners were at work.

4. I Go to TRANSFER

A GREEN PARTITION OPEN AT THE TOP separated Transfer from Collating. All other work groups could see each other unless the stair well and commodious Ladies' Room in the middle of the building interfered. This central portion blocked my view of Backs. I felt rather lonely not to be able to see my "friends," but the married women in Transfer made me feel right at home. They worked 'til two or three o'clock when the bobby-sox high school girls came in. FAT, who sat beside me, said she came in after her children left for school and would be home before they returned.

"It's very nice," she went on. "There's no feeling of pressure. I can stay home on school holidays and times when the children need me. . . . They have the most consideration for the workers here of any place I know. If you make a mistake, they never 'say anything.' Of course, if you do *too* much, they would. There is *no pressure* here. . . . The only thing is the work doesn't stimulate your mind. It gets automatic. You tend to daydream but have to pay some attention."

She welcomed music for relief and said, "I'll take *any kind*. . . .

34

After a while this work makes me get sleepy. The music gives me a lift. Somehow it seems as though certain colors, like these magenta numbers, put you to sleep after you've worked on them for days and the music lifts you up again."

After copying figures for an hour, I felt slowed down. FAT was rechecking my work and she tried to encourage me by telling me that I hadn't made any mistakes so far. She said, "Now you see what I mean by *monotony*. . . . After we finish one group, we take it up to the front of the room. We *could* wait and stack them up at our seat but we *like the excuse to move.* The girls sharpen pencils and so on to get out of the seat. Otherwise we'd use our eyes every minute."

After another quarter-hour of work, my back began to feel tired. My eyes felt a little heavy. My pep was gone and I felt *deadened by monotony.* I said to FAT, "I feel draggy."

She answered, "Oh, you'll get that feeling."

To "get out of the seat," as FAT had expressed it, I went up to see my friends in Backs. They seemed much more tired and quieter than in the morning, but not unfriendly. I told them I had been doing transferring. "I couldn't *stand* that," one of them said. "It's so boring. *Our* work has *variety*." Other workers in Backs nodded agreement.

I didn't spend long in Backs as I knew I must get back to Transfer where a THIN high school girl had taken FAT's place a little before three o'clock. If I was to experience the full impact of boredom, I must stay on the job. My new neighbor was pleasant and smiled at me. She said, "I like the music *very* much! It (nodding at the stack of transfer papers) gets so boring." I managed a wry smile in return. I felt draggy and tired at that point.

When FAT and I were working together, the room had been relatively *quiet*. I had enjoyed the musical program which was brighter than the one in the morning. One girl had sharpened her pencil to the rhythm of a waltz and another had walked by jauntily to the lilt of "Oh, Susanna." One waltz with a pronounced beat did irritate me while I was trying to learn a new procedure and another loud piece with a pronounced beat made me forget to move the consumer sales to the top, but all in all distractions had been at a minimum.

Now it was different. As FAT had warned me, "When the high school girls come in, it gets pretty noisy. They talk and chatter 'til I don't know how they know what they're doing. They're eating candy and apples all over the place."

My new neighbor, THIN, offered me a Life Saver. She said, "They don't mind if you bring in things to eat but not ice cream—*it drips!*"

The supervisor of Transfer and Collating explained to me later that many of the bobby-soxers came right from school, and to avoid noisy, heavy "traffic" to the cafeteria the company preferred to let them bring in something to eat. "I'd rather have them eat than talk," the supervisor said in a rather desperately resigned way.

Yes, the young people were definitely more restless than the older women. The girl in front of me had an apple ready for consumption. The very THIN girl behind me took up *all* her pencils to sharpen: she had quite a handful. The girl on my left had laid a half-eaten bar of candy on her desk and was busy putting on lipstick. Then she combed her hair. A few minutes afterwards she got up and went to the Ladies' Room. She finally returned and settled down to eating popcorn out of a cellophane bag. . . . Her eyes were stare-y. She came back to earth and talked to the girl across the table. At long last she put a carbon under her sheet of paper and finally pushed out some work!

I could begin to understand why the three-quarter partition had been put up to separate Transfer and Collating where the high school boys worked. Even with this precaution, the supervisor told me at times the boys climbed over the top to see the girls.

It was perhaps not surprising to find that Helen, the supervisor responsible for both Transfer and Collating, was less tranquil than the supervisor of Backs. Helen was a trusted, old-time worker with the company and quite understandably looked back wistfully to "the good old days" before wartime personnel problems and part-time workers came on the scene.

Helen was THIN and active about her supervisory duties. She did not care for the music herself as she said it bothered her. When it was first considered, she said she was against it. "Why not give the girls a raise instead?" she had suggested. However, after seeing music tried, although she didn't enjoy it herself, she said she wouldn't "dare" to take it out—the workers liked it so much. Like Lorna she knew the job and said, "The girls like it (the music) but with *that* kind of work they'd welcome *any* distraction."

After working in Transfer, I could see why it had lowest prestige among the different sections and why the personnel manager had told me that they tried to avoid backward movement—as to Transfer—of employees from higher paying and ranking jobs. Transfer work had least interest and lowest pay, and the group of teen-age beginners would annoy an established, disciplined worker.

Several considerations explained the company's leniency with the young Transfer workers. It was a starting job and some excellent training material came from the bobby-sox group. Also, in general, young people were more alert than older ones, the personnel man said, and once broken in would stay longer on a boring job because they hadn't had the experience of doing work they liked. For these reasons management was willing to overlook the restless afternoons in Transfer!

5. A Change to COMPTOMETERS

IT WAS A DECIDED CHANGE when I went to the orderly Comptometer Section at 7:45 next morning. As I came in, the opening musical program was on. Several lively marches made me feel peppy. Some people had come early and were already at work. The supervisor showed me the sheets with their columns of figures and explained the comptometer procedure to me. I felt challenged by the new task.

I was sorry when the stimulating marches which had greeted me were abandoned and a step-down to softer, less colorful music was put in, apparently, *for work*. It was early in the morning, and when the music droned out "Melancholy Baby," I felt let down. I looked around to see how the other comp workers were reacting to this musical undercut in our first series of selections. They appeared unperturbed on the surface as they maintained their steady comptometer performance. These were seasoned workers.

One older MUSCULAR-FAT caught my attention, while FATS were fairly common and there were a good many MODERATE MIXTURES. Although some THINS were present, they were not extreme and were more sedate than the hyperactive high school girls who had been so much in evidence the afternoon before. I settled down to serious work.

There was virtually *no talking*—not because there was any rule against it but because the figuring couldn't be done when there was conversation. Workers were using the comp machines all the time except when fixing pencils, laying out new stacks of sheets, or tending to other brief matters. Because of the lack of sociability, I gave my attention mainly to effects of the music on the work. This problem was of particular interest to the company as they did not want to add any extraneous irritant to annoy these concentrated workers. As in all departments, accuracy was of paramount importance. Errors were costly.

In the Ladies' Room I met a girl from the comp section on the third floor; I was glad to have a chance to talk with her. She said she wished they had music on her floor, that they play it in comp school. For adding it should have a *steady even beat,* she said. It worked out well in school where they were all doing the same thing.

I recalled reading in the manual the supervisor had given me: *"COMPTOMETER—Rhythmic Action—In performing addition the movements of the hand and forearm should be timed to insure smooth, regular action. Rhythmic action is just as essential in learning to operate the Calculator as it is in learning to play a musical instrument."*[4] My new friend told me she hums to herself when adding. However, multiplication and division do not *fit the rhythm* as adding does, she said.

I had a chance to ask one of the comp workers in the Checking Department what she thought about the effect of the rhythm of the music on her comp work. She replied, "At first it seems funny, then you *get used to it* as it plays through the day. . . . Sometimes when I'm dividing and the music is playing, I get confused."

The personnel manager had told me the "key press" people in

[4]Manual of Instruction for Burroughs Calculator, Lesson 1.

another department had refused music because it upset their work rhythm. I noticed on the 4:40 musical program at the end of the day that my moderately FAT neighbor lost count when she was trying to hit a key a certain number of times. The waltz, "Tales from the Vienna Woods," was playing. She counted in a whisper 1 to 6, then 1 to 5. Then she frowned as though she had made an error. She looked at the clock and stopped work for several minutes.

Another neighbor seemed to be doing a waltz of her own as she comped in three-to-one time to some pieces. She must have been something of a "virtuoso" as a speed-up at the end didn't throw her off. She was able to make her work rhythm fit in with the music.

As for myself, I was unable to do this. Pieces made me feel wonderful when they "went with" my speed, while others that were draggy, fast, or with an odd rhythm gave me a feeling of musical interference. Slow passages in a fast piece made me feel as though I was working *against* the music. I found the amount of effort I had to put in varied with the musical "accompaniment." With practice, I might be able to "rise above" the music or fit in with it like my three-to-one neighbor. However, in the long run a regular rhythm suited to my usual operating speed should prove to be less complicating and less tiring.

After about three-quarters of an hour, I began to notice signs of fatigue not so much from the music as from the mechanics of the job itself. My neck and right arm were tired from pressing the keys. Workers said their arms tired when they worked long and *under pressure*. After looking at the columns of figures for about an hour, my eyes began to feel tired too.

To rest myself by a change of position, I leaned back in the chair which had an adjustable, tipping back. It felt good! To change the focus of my eyes I looked away at distant chimneys. I was in the middle of the room where I couldn't get a view of the grass and gardens. I wished there was a blossoming plant somewhere—in a pot or hanging basket—to cheer me. I put the palms of my hands over my eyes to give them a little rest.

As a novice, I felt restless and looked around to see if anyone else seemed to feel so too. One girl got up and went to speak to the girl behind her. She was eating something. It reminded me of the varied activities in Transfer, but this sort of thing was most unusual in the Comptometer Section. None of the other regular workers got up. The one who was walking around was THINnest of the group.

The MODERATE MIXTURE on my left had a bad cold. She said, "I'm surprised that I feel like working today."

I couldn't help wondering whether this same worker in an annoying work situation might not have been a "natural" for absenteeism. As it was, the work situation in Comps was quiet and pleasant. There was no heckling by supervision. In other words, if a worker of average strength was a little below par, the job situation wasn't too hard to take. In fact, it might be more cheerful than to stay home "nursing a cold." At least our MODERATE MIXTURE had not been tempted to stay away.

When I left the Comptometer Section, I felt I was leaving an extremely satisfactory work group. As to effects of music on the work, it seemed to me there should be more tests run to ascertain the optimum tempo for the majority of workers and that programming should try to achieve a smooth, even rhythm in pieces for this group. Comptometer workers enjoyed the music immensely. The MODERATE MIXTURE behind me said, "I *love* the music. When I came in in the summer I thought they should have *something*. . . . This work isn't very interesting."

In justice to the Comp workers, it should be noted that their job certainly lacked variety. However, figuring and comp pressing occupied the attention more than the deadening monotony of Transfer or relative lack of interest in Backs. I think the behavior of the Comp workers bore this out. As I had been told, work in Comptometer was "different" and "separate."

6. SIGNS and DEALS

I WAS INTERESTED TO SEE HOW the two remaining parts of the regular work sequence, Signs (Signs and Additions) and Deals, compared with the sections I had been in. There was a lull in work in Signs. Company policy was to require regular attendance of workers at their desks, but to let them read or write letters until a new set of field data was available. The job consisted of making inventories from the field data.

Work was very similar to Backs and, as already mentioned, carried a similar "middle-class" work status. People graduated from Transfer into Signs *or* Backs. Both sections were located near the windows on the same side of the room. I think Backs workers would agree with the way a woman in Signs summed up the situation, "We're in pleasant physical surroundings, but the work is monotonous."

Deals lay in the corridor section between Backs and Signs. Desks were two deep next to the windows to leave a passageway by the stair well. All desks gave a view into trees and sky line, and desks right by the windows gave the same pleasing glimpse into neighborhood gardens that I had enjoyed my first morning in Backs.

As I knew that Deals was the "top" job in the Checking Department, I wanted to learn just what it involved and to have a chance to work at it. The supervisor said the drug product class they were on was more complex than most other groups—that complexity and muddles were likely to occur. Usually they just turned pages looking to see whether "deal" was present. If so, they circled it. Often it was *not* present; therefore the main occupation was *turning sheets!* They looked through fronts and backs and used the comp a little but not often.

There was no problem in the use of music for this section. Workers liked music and it didn't conflict with the work; in fact, it was *welcomed* as they turned pages. They turned pages so much of the time that many of the girls used a rubber cap on one finger for flipping pages more easily. All pieces helped to relieve boredom, and there was no difficulty of a counter rhythm in this job as in the Comp section. Workers liked odd "variety" numbers like "In a Persian Market." During a smooth section of the piece, several workers whistled along with the melody. When a Strauss waltz was playing, I thought it was pleasing but not very stimulating. However, I found myself tapping my heels to the rhythm and enjoying a little bright *optimistic* reverie. I felt a certain air of gaiety about the music which I was able to enjoy while turning pages in Deals.

There was very little talking. It didn't seem that the nature of the work could account for this. However, a noticeable lack of sociable, talkative FATS as compared with other sections might have made a difference. Also, there were quite a few mature THINS in Deals. They were not bursting with youthful exuberance like the THIN Transfer girl just let out of school and, if anything, gave an impression of social inhibition.

Doubtless during their period of work training since Transfer days, they had been rewarded and promoted for steady work habits and felt, with good reason, that reticence was an asset in this type of work. Workers would discuss problems that came up in connection with the work but did not engage in conversations with each other. A little after noon, two girls near the window rested themselves by "looking away." They took off their glasses and daydreamed a bit. Otherwise pages turned unceasingly throughout the section until it was time for lunch.

As we went out, a THIN worker from Deals said to me, "The music 'perks you up' at times, especially after lunch." The noon music program had begun before we stopped work. In Deals a novelty "music box" arrangement of a rhumba was a welcome diversion! I shuddered to think what such a piece might have done to the rhythm of my work in the Comp section and wondered whether the afternoon in Collating would be as "different" from the regular checking groups as my experience in Comptometer.

7. COLLATING
or
Behind the Green Partition

I WAS CURIOUS TO SEE WHAT lay behind the green partition which had screened my view of Collating when I was working in Transfer. I ate lunch hurriedly so that I could go "behind the screens." I was glad I had chosen afternoon as the high school boys, who would work full-time in the summer, came only in the afternoon. There were six boys and several girls at work when I arrived. The work section was lighted by windows which overlooked the street. The atmosphere seemed pleasant and, to my surprise, rather stimulating. This was a change.

The boys were walking around putting pages of reports into ordered piles or going to pull "holdouts" from the files. They sat at the file drawer while they were "pulling," and occasionally someone sat down to check numbers. Otherwise most people were active and *in motion*. This was *not* sedentary work, and no one was continually "tied to a desk." Work was full of action compared to the pencil-and-paper desk work I had been doing. Even one girl working on records had fly sheets and was stapling, counting, and recounting papers. Most jobs had some sort of activity and required frequent change of position.

Middle-aged Mrs. Santom, the immediate one in charge of Collating (under Helen's general supervision) was busy overseeing her bounding crew. The boys got to talking in a lively fashion and she said, "Sh- sh" in a way which appeared like a more-or-less habitual technique for reducing the amount of gaiety. Good cheer was rampant and the boys liked to joke and kid. It would have *shocked* the solemn workers in Deals! One boy who was pulling out records called to me, "Lend me a dollar. *We* work at Filetab."

Another boy who was walking around a table stacking papers when a slow piece was playing said, "We *want something fast.* These make us feel like slowing down." He "drooped" his shoulders and slouched along as he collated and made everyone laugh. "They're mostly young kids on the fourth floor—Transfer and all," he went on, "and they want something *fast!*" Apparently, to this young man the Checking Department beyond the partitions was mainly composed of beauteous bobby-soxers with fresh lipstick on! I could see Mrs. Santom coming in to find him climbing over the wall! Nevertheless he was certainly correct as to the slowness of the music for Collating.

The music not only seemed slow in this section, but with only one loudspeaker, it was a little soft. One boy who was lifting heavy, filled drawers of a file cabinet got little encouragement from the soft, smooth, dreamy rendering of "Silver Moon," even though in the ratings of a music record house this was listed as a "good," if not "excellent," number. To evaluate the excellence of a given piece, I was convinced the *function* of the music must be understood, for "one man's meat might be another man's poison": I felt the man and the situation would have to be understood before prescribing what music would be "good" for anybody on any job. Whether a piece would be called "good" or "excellent" should depend on a knowledge of "good" *for what*—what people, what age, what job—under what conditions.

In Collating when we heard "Seventh Heaven" after "Deep Night," "Silver Moon," and "Brown Bird Singing," the atmosphere was so smooth and dreamy I stopped observing and gazed out of the window daydreaming! The two boys who were collating seemed to be *pushing* to pick up the papers. There was no peppy rhythm to their gait as there had been earlier *before the music came on*. One of the boys said, "What we need is dance music. I can see us collating to dance music!" Even jive might be all right for Collating although, I was told, it made the sedentary bobby-soxers in Transfer jump around in their seats.

Collating, even more than Comps, was "separate" and "different" from the other sections of the Checking Department. I felt as though the MUSCULAR high school boys had given me a tonic. Management said they were hired because they could lift sixty-pound file cabinets. They were certainly different organisms from the mature, inhibited THINS in the "high-hat" Deals section!—and they were doing a different job in a different way and needed *different* music. I was now in a position to make comparisons, as I had been in all sections of the Checking Department.

8. I Work AT NIGHT

ONE NEW EXPERIENCE WAS LEFT FOR ME in the Checking Department—to see the same jobs performed *at night!* Would the situation seem the same?

Night workers were older men and women who held other jobs during the day. Many came early right from their first job and ate supper in the cafeteria. They were glad to get a tasty supper for a low price and have a chance to visit with Filetab friends. Most of the group were highly intelligent men and women who held responsible jobs during the day. A number of young married women wearing large diamonds probably had husbands in the service. They all considered the night work a sort of diversion. For this reason they particularly liked having music. Many said they listened to radio at home evenings so they might as well be "doing something" while they listened.

And the pay was good. Night workers got time-and-a-half pay, as did day workers who worked over forty hours a week. Extra day work on Saturday morning was optional unless there was a particular rush on. Workers who wanted to earn a little more money welcomed the chance. Saturday morning and night workers both had the rather exhilarating feeling that they were voluntarily doing something "extra" for which they were well rewarded.

This atmosphere greeted me when I arrived on the fourth floor at seven o'clock. Mr. Hall, the department manager in charge of the fourth floor, explained to me that he was just there for this evening, as different executives took turns a night at a time. He also explained that there were no set "supervisors" for the night group. Management just named one of the workers to "pass out work." Workers liked this lack of "official" supervision. When they had to meet a date for a particular deadline, they'd really pitch in, the manager said. However, most of the time they didn't have to push it too hard.

I thought I'd start out in Backs as I had in the daytime. At 7:00 P. M. it was still light outside, and the setting seemed just about as it had in the morning. However, there were fewer people in all sections and the room seemed sparsely filled. Workers were apt to skip several nights a week, I was told, especially Friday nights and summer evenings when they went to the lake. Management allowed for this in its planning.

Of those present, there was a good percentage of men. A few were MUSCULAR with a good number FAT or MUSCULAR-FAT. One THIN male trainee who worked full-time stood out in contrast to most of the other men. Many were MODERATE MIXTURES. I noticed several THIN women, and MUSCULAR-FATS were quite common. The general tone of the whole group reminded me of the mature day workers in Comptometer.

The music sounded softer than it had with more people in the room. Sometimes it was really *too* soft and you had to strain to hear it. The man who had been chosen to "pass out work" in Backs didn't have to raise his voice while the music was on to have people hear his cheery remarks.

To me he said, "This is probably the best place to work in the whole city. They never use 'the old whip' on you. . . . People talk and don't work in fear of losing their job, but they turn out the work. Probably that's the way to run an office."

To another woman he said, "You feel 'peppy' tonight."

To another, "You were the only person to do a perfect bundle the first time. I tried to find you last night to tell you."

It was interesting to see how the carefully designed policy of the personnel executive was reflected in turn by Mr. Hall, the department head, and then by the man with whom I had just been talking. Mr. Hall said to me later in the evening, "If you 'whip,' the errors mount. If they can take their own pace, it's okay; but when they're pressed, the errors mount and it makes more work in the end. If a person is very slow, it's better to let them go than to try to speed them up—due to the errors."

I recalled the policy on errors as the personnel manager had explained it to me. He had said that they never placed the blame for an error on any *one* person. If a mistake was discovered, it was simply announced that an error had been found and that the work would have to be rechecked or done over. This policy of not "fixing blame" in particular instances was appreciated by workers in that they were spared the fear of humiliation. This resulted in decreased tension during work and very likely resulted in fewer total errors and in more contented workers.

Certainly, the night group who had experience doing work under *other* conditions and *other* personnel policies recognized some of the advantages which young workers might have taken for granted. These able night people enjoyed their work. They were very noticeably thinking more about the meaning of the figures than the day group and used logic to avoid errors. For instance, when there were questions of decision as to prices which went with pounds and ounces or values of bottles of pills, they didn't let errors slip through that would make a few pills cost more than the regular price of several bottles.

Night Backs was even gayer than the day section and even more enthusiastic about the music, but needed a louder setting for night.

Like day workers, they wanted greater variety in the selections. As a boy in Collating had said to me, "You can *kill* any piece!"

Night workers would have liked the music played later. While they were free to leave any time after ten o'clock, many stayed until 11:30 or 11:45. The night manager joked that he was the new janitor as he stayed 'til twelve to close up the building. A jolly MUSCULAR-FAT man said with a smile, "When they play "Til We Meet Again' at 11:00 P. M. and we have three-quarters of an hour to go, it's not so good!"

As there was no Collating going on and I knew the similarity to Backs of the work in Signs and Deals, I spent most of the rest of the time in the Comp section. It was about 8:15 when I arrived there. I wrote in my notes: "It is getting dark outside. The music seems to *cheer* the atmosphere inside as the darkness gathers. . . . The pieces seem louder than earlier in the evening. . . . As it gets darker outside, it seems brighter inside. The noise of the comptometers sounds friendly and reassuring. . . . I can see how this atmosphere is preferable to a 'lonely' evening."

I could see why workers liked having music as night settled down over the big building. As one girl said, "Oh, everyone loves the music. We hate to have it off for even a few minutes." And a supervisor remarked feelingly, "People who work all day like to have music at night. After all, they've already done one day's work."

However, when a group of us went to the basement lounge for cokes at the set rest period from 9:00 to 9:15, a man who did comp work made a comment similar to some of the day group. "When you push eight or nine times," he said, "you get to thinking about the music and lose count."

Another worker mentioned the fact that the girls who worked on Tables upstairs did a lot of figuring. "They voted *not* to have music," she said.

The man who acted as supervisor for Comps had told me he was so busy answering questions he didn't hear the music himself. For this reason, supervisors probably didn't mind the fact that the music wasn't very loud at night. However, soft music at night—particularly when it was *slow* like "Santa Lucia" or "Sweet and Low"—affected me like a lullaby. I was glad when a few peppy tempos came on at quarter of eleven. They sounded nice at that late hour. I wondered if the program for night shouldn't include increasingly bright numbers as it grew later. Where this wouldn't interfere with the work, it would be very cheering. Heavy, mournful, or draggy pieces certainly should be avoided—as well as lullabies!

A THIN young man who was being trained for an executive job (the male trainee) had been in the Checking Department all day and evening. He had noticed that I'd been working from 8:00 A. M. to 11:00 P. M. and, during the last group of selections, came over to speak to me. He showed a friendly attitude and talked a little about the company. "I've never found as many nice people under one roof," he said. "Probably there's no other place in the world like it! I've never met *anyone* here I didn't like. Everyone is *so* pleasant—even top management—they're so *friendly* to you."

As I looked back over my experiences of the past few days, I agreed with him and with the policy which the personnel director had outlined to me, "By constant vigilance we try to keep a work atmosphere free from threat and anxiety where workers can work and feel happy and secure."

9. WHAT People WHERE?

YOU WILL SEE THAT THE KINDS OF PEOPLE in the different sections of the Checking Department (Tables 12 and 13) reflect the human situations I felt when I was with the various groups. The following sentences summarize some of the major points:

MEN

Over half of the Collating boys were MUSCULAR—more than five times the incidence for college men.

Night men in the sample showed *high* incidence of FAT, MUSCULAR-FAT, and MODERATE MIXTURE as compared with either college or Collating men.

WOMEN

Transfer, Signs, and Comptometer had well *over the average* number of FATS. In Transfer, incidence was extreme for the older women.

Backs had an *average* number of FATS.

Deals had *no* FATS.

Deals had an exceptionally *high* percentage of THINS (71%).

53

TABLE 12

Men

Male Office Workers Compared with College Men				
Collating 7	Others 4	Night 10		College men 4000
0%	0%	10%	Fat	4%
0%	0%	30%	Muscular-fat	13%
57%	0%	10%	Muscular	11%
14%	0%	0%	Muscular-thin	16%
14%	25%	0%	Thin	9.5%
0%	0%	0%	Plump-delicate	7%
14%	75%	50%	Moderate mixture	39.5%

Transfer and Comptometer had an *average* number of THINS.
    Bobby-soxers in Transfer had more THINS than the older women.
Signs and Backs had *less than average* incidence of THINS.
Others (which included supervisors) had a *high* incidence of MOD-
    ERATE MIXTURES and MUSCULAR-THINS.
Except for more FATS, Transfer bobby-soxers and Comptometer had
    close to an average assortment of women as compared with the
    727.

    It is natural for us to want to know more and to under-
stand more about the *meaning* of the behavior of the workers we
have just met. We have seen these groups in action. Why do they
act as they do?

    I think it will be best to describe another situation and another
set of workers and then compare the comments of the two groups
in relation to some of the problems common to them all. Then we
shall be able to tell better whether the reaction is due to the worker
or to the work situation in which he finds himself, or to what extent
it results from a combination of the two factors.

    Let's go to a factory (Part III) and once more work and watch
and listen. Will the story be entirely different from what we have
just experienced? Will people have all different feelings in a factory?
Will all people feel different? How can we know unless we find out?

TABLE 13

WOMEN

	WOMEN OFFICE WORKERS COMPARED WITH 727 WOMEN								
	Transfer 29	Transfer Bobby-soxers 25	Signs 14	Backs 27	Deals 7	Comptometer 33	Others 8	Night 10	Women 727
FAT	45%	28%	28.57%	18.52%	0%	24%	12.5%	10%	17%
MUSCULAR-FAT	10%	12%	7%	11%	0%	12%	0%	20%	11%
MUSCULAR	3%	4%	14%	4%	14%	6%	0%	0%	6%
MUSCULAR-THIN	3%	4%	0%	7%	0%	3%	12.5%	20%	5%
THIN	17%	20%	14%	7%	71%	24%	12.5%	30%	21%
PLUMP-DELICATE	0%	0%	0%	11%	0%	0%	0%	0%	4%
MODERATE MIXTURE	21%	32%	36%	41%	14%	30%	62.5%	20%	35%

55

PART III - IN A FACTORY

INTRODUCTION

AN INDUSTRIAL CITY IS QUITE DIFFERENT from a residential suburb. A downtown factory among other factory buildings near railroad tracks—even with a stream nearby—creates a different work atmosphere. Available workers were different from the relatively homogeneous suburbanites at Filetab.

Originally, Yankees made up the population of this New England city, but a strong Irish group had been brought in to work in the first mill. French Canadians soon followed when the mill realized they could be imported for less money. At the time of our study (1945), Irish and French Canadians vied for political power in the city. Later comers, Poles and Greeks, were still minority groups.

Of the 650 employed at Textron, three-quarters were French (French Canadian). A good number of Greek and Polish were in the remaining quarter. Six hundred of the employees were women. The men were employed as mechanics, floorsweepers, doormen, cutters, in a few other minor jobs, and as executives. The average age of the women was 35, although the range was from 16-year-old high school girls to women 65.

I went to work the first morning eager to experience this new human setting, eager to meet the stitchers on the third floor where it seemed best for me to concentrate my study. This floor had been reconverted from wartime production of jungle hammocks or parachutes to the peacetime silk and lace of women's slips.

10. I Begin to STITCH

"YOU CAN'T EVER MAKE PIECE RATES ON DARTS," the girl in the washroom told me. She turned to the older woman beside her. "Remember when you did. You nearly killed yourself." She looked at me again. "No. It's so much an hour. You won't do better than that."

It was my first day of stitching and Darts was the learners' job. My shoulders drooped at the prospect of my impossible task. I had started out in good spirits, then the thread began to break every two minutes. I felt discouraged. Now I felt even more so, but I must hurry back. They wouldn't want me long in the washroom.

The picture flashed through my mind of the THIN girl I had seen crying as she was "separated." The somewhat MUSCULAR supervisor informed me, "THIN girls are nervous. They *cry* if the thread breaks twice." While I wasn't especially THIN, but more of a MODERATE MIXTURE, I could appreciate how the THIN girl must have felt and why the job was not for her. Would I be able to make the grade?

The thread trouble kept up pretty constantly from 10:00 to

11:00. Jeanie oversaw my work. I stitched on scraps, piecing them together to make yokes. Jeanie was good and tried to find the reason for the breaks. There was a burr on the needle so she brought a new one and I put it in. The threads still broke. Before this, the girl behind me (the Service Girl) had oiled the little up-curve of the bobbin. This had only soiled the material but had not remedied the breaking.

Jeanie came back and analyzed the fact that the breaks seemed to be occurring *between* pieces of material rather than while stitching the cloth itself. Therefore she concluded that I was making too many chain stitches between different sections of the pieces of cloth and that I should make fewer. Perhaps this would stop the breaking. I began to feel encouraged even though my eyes were tired. I thought we had tracked down the source of the difficulty.

Lunch came at 11:15. I went down with a kindly married FAT who took me under her wing when I asked her if she could tell me the way to the lunch room. She showed me the ropes. "You spend half your lunch hour standing in line," she informed me. She was on a six-hour shift so had only thirty minutes for lunch. It took about ten to get through the cafeteria counter.

The food was tempting and reasonably priced. The big room was light and cheerful. I expressed my pleasure, as I was hungry. "Yes, it's good to go to eat," FAT replied, "but it's a long time 'til you get home at six when you eat lunch at 11:15—and some of the girls eat at 11:00 and don't leave until 5:00."

FAT and her rather THIN friend, Peg, sat across from me at one of the long eating tables. When I told the girls about my trouble with the thread's breaking and how Jeanie had helped me, one of them said, "Oh, Jeanie, she's swell. She'll remember you for a job you want. But Irene! Irene is a stinker. She gets behind you and watches every move you make."

FAT said she loved to sew—always had. She loved to stitch and also loved to *sit*. "It's just too good to be true to be *paid* to do just what you like to do anyway! But I never get up to my quote.

I used to let that trouble me a good deal, but the supervisor told me 'they' didn't care anyway, so now I don't worry about it."

Peg worked on lace. She acted alert but not tense and said she liked her job. She was only moderately THIN and friendly. Her brown eyes invited conversation, but there wasn't time for much of a chat as they had to hurry with lunch to be back on the line again.

FAT did most of the talking. She told us about the evening dress she would like to make herself for the installation of the Rebekahs in two weeks. Also how she was a "Vice-Grand." She vouchsafed the fact, which she had been whispering to others, that she was out yesterday because she had to run a meeting of the Lodge in the absence of the "Grand."

I still had fifteen minutes left when they had to go. I was on an eight-hour day, and so got forty-five minutes. I went to the wash-room. I noticed my lower eyelids were reddened. My eyes felt heavy and I rather dreaded to use them all afternoon. The light was excellent—adequate overhead lighting and a little light on the machine itself, but the vibration of the machine made the light jiggle which resulted in a "moving" light focussed on the work.

As I took my seat behind the machine, the girl behind me said, "It's the afternoon that drags. The morning goes by fast, but time drags in the afternoon." However, the solution of the thread's breaking helped a great deal. With short spaces between pieces of cloth, the thread did not break. Also a program of lively marches and Army Air Corps selections came over at one o'clock and did wonders for my lagging spirit. They seemed to steady me as I did the stitching, and I felt it went more evenly and faster.

There was more music around two and I enjoyed this. However after the Victory shift of high school girls came in around 2:30, there was so much more noise and the vibration of machines was so much greater that I couldn't hear the music except as an addition to the jumble of noise. By then, I was working on real production piecework and the added racket was not welcome. Before the

Victory workers came in, the male singers came over well enough to be enjoyable on some pieces. After the added noise, the singing was "just another blur."

The Victory shift girl on my left was very helpful to me and friendly. She said she didn't like to stitch darts and didn't especially enjoy the work anyway, I judged. She said they were very particular, especially if you had *Irene* judge your work.

One girl who was doing Zig Zag mending on lace said her eyes felt terrible—as though they had been spanked. I found that if I looked away—out of the window when it was open—it rested my eyes to change focus. I asked if she ever looked up from the work. She said, "No."

I said, "Of course, you don't want to take the time." She nodded. She would probably have had the same reaction if I had suggested putting the palms of her hands over her eyes to give them a little rest. I had found this helped too, but of course it took time. The way she had said "No" made me realize this sort of solution was "out of the question" in her mind.

II. I STITCH Some More

NEXT DAY I GOT TO WORK A FEW MINUTES EARLY. I went to the washroom. A woman came up to me. She said if I wanted to know what made nervous fatigue, she could tell me it was the "piece rates" and the feeling of working under pressure. She said she had worked in other places without piece rates and it hadn't tired her nervously anything like now.

When I got to my machine, there was a new woman in my row. She said she left Lace Zig Zag last night because it made her so nervous. She had come up to our floor from downstairs where she had been working on jungle hammocks (war work). It was heavy as compared to the lace, but the lace was much more nerve-racking, she said.

"They pull apart the lace after you've done it," she explained. "It's all uneven so it tears and then they bring it back to you. It's so discouraging. It made me so nervous. The pay was high and they gave the job to some of us who were coming up from downstairs. But what's the money if you get so nervous. I cried last night and said I couldn't stand it any longer. They shifted me over here

[Darts]." When I asked her if people ever had their hands tremble
and feel unsteady, she said, "Oh, yes."

From 8:00 to 9:00 I waited to get started, as I wanted to start
the pile right and Irene was busy with another woman. I went over
to her and asked her how I could tell which way to start the pile.
From the way she said, "I'll come over and see after *I'm* through
with this woman," I knew I had done something out of line. At
lunch, they told me *the worker is never supposed to leave her seat.*
If you want help, you call the first name of the supervisor.

Irene came over eventually. I got started, but I still did not feel
confident about analyzing the way of the "grain" of the cloth. I
had been told a number of ways, and each time the cloth was turned
differently so one method would not work. Therefore I tried my own
way of "earmarking" by lifting a corner of the next piece to show
which way it should be done. By ten o'clock, I felt very nervously
tired and "under strain." My hand did not feel as steady and I did
not feel confident about the work.

About this time some rather fast and jumpy music came over
and it did not make me feel better. The rhythm was definitely
irritating. The fact that I could hear it very well, as the Victory
shift wasn't in, made it all the more annoying. The jittery tempo
did not help my work as the marches had the day before. Even
piano selections later in the morning still did not affect me in a
pleasant way.

At last the bell rang for lunch. As I was gathering up my work,
my FAT friend several rows in front of me turned around as she
left her machine. She called to me, "Aren't you coming?" suggesting
I walk along with her. This pleased me. She advised, "Take
the work out of the machine when you leave. Some grease might
get on it." Her whole attitude was friendly.

Going in to lunch, we were greeted by some "dancy" music. It had
a bright rhythm. The woman behind me in line made some
little dance steps and seemed to be enjoying it. She was a cheerful
woman who pushed a truck all day. She said she liked moving

around. Her husband was dead and her boys in the service, so she had taken the job. She asked where I was living. I said in a room I got through the USO Industrial. This seemed all right with her. However, she wanted to impress me with the fact that she was "well fixed." She said she had made over "one of her summer places" to live in. Peg came over to the line. A milk shake was all she bought because she always brings a sandwich and other things from home.

At lunch I asked Peg and my FAT friend what the custom was about the washroom. They said, "You can go out for ten minutes in the morning and ten minutes in the afternoon." I said they hadn't said anything to me about it. "Well," they said, "that's how they do. They don't tell you, but if you stay out more than ten minutes, the supervisor will speak to you."

I asked Peg if her hands ever tended to tremble and told her I had felt shaky early that morning. She said, "What helps me the most is to eat a little something. I take up a cookie or something and eat it around two o'clock." I asked how she did this as I understood you weren't supposed to eat at work. It soiled materials. Once army inspectors had found chocolate stains on the parachutes.

"Oh, I eat in the washroom," she replied. "That's what they all do. . . . It's good to get up and walk down, too. That helps some." She insisted on giving me one of her chocolate cookies to eat right away and one for two o'clock. She wrapped it in a napkin for me. I felt mean to take both her chocolate cookies, but she assured me, "There are plenty more at home."

I asked them what the story was as to "talking" on the job. I told them I noticed that when I asked the girl next to me a question or talked to her, the supervisor would come over and ask if she could help me. They said, "Yes, you'll find out a lot of things if you work here long enough. They don't say it right out, but you find out. They don't want you to talk on the job, and they'll speak to you if they see you do it much."

This agreed with the reply I got from the Victory shift high school girl the day before when I asked her about "talking." She had said, "You're not supposed to."

Then when I asked, "Does *she* [the supervisor] speak to you if you do?" she answered, "Yes. Well—when she did, I went beyond 'the limit.' You know us high school girls—we'd talk *all* the time!"

I had several minutes after lunch before time to go back to the job, so I went to the Smoking Room. They said you could go there whether you smoked or not. I was met by dark-green wainscoting, with glaring white walls above it. The fact that only unfinished wooden chairs and a crude bench of a table furnished the room made the walls unduly prominent. Although a few ash trays were provided, cigarette butts had been stamped out on the pitted floor. Windows on three sides—two sides onto the workroom and one onto the street—gave one a fishbowl feeling. I could see why the room was little used.

The matron of the washroom was one of the few people there. We visited a little. She said she tried to stitch a year and a half ago but it "got on her nerves." "They were just beginning and everyone told me a different way to do it. 'Hold it this way,' one would say. Then another would say, 'Hold it that way.' It was terrible. I couldn't stand it: it made me so nervous. One day there were five people watching me work. The time-study man and four people, one on each side. There were always four people watching. I couldn't stand it. I cried. I would have had a nervous breakdown if I'd stayed doing that. After two weeks they let me come in here [pointing to the washroom]. No one checks me here. There are too many people on your neck 'out there' [pointing to the workroom]. That's the trouble, there are too many supervisors."

It was time to work again. I dreaded to go back. The windows had been closed all morning and you couldn't see a thing but the blue and white paint on the panes. Only when the sun shone very brightly could you see the red buildings through some light places in the brushmarks. It was a pleasant surprise to find one window opened about a foot. The glimpse of green trees and red brick mills looked like a little oil painting. Textron had one side of the building beside a stream with leafy trees on its edge. The neighboring red factories took on artistic value in this setting. I wished I could see more than the one-foot canvas! The outdoors was strengthening to taut nerves, and the associations it brought to mind were optimistic. I plunged into the work with renewed courage.

At 2:30 I went to the washroom and timed myself exactly as to the ten-minute allowance. I ate my chocolate cookie. Another girl near the washbowls was eating potato chips out of a box. As I went out, I took a second to talk with a girl who stitched on Straps.

She said she liked the work and didn't get nearly as tired as being Service Girl. "When I did that, I had to go right to bed as soon as I got home," she said. "The tiring thing about Straps is trying to make the quota—fifty-two packages of twenty-four [three each] straps. *You can't stop a minute.*" It reminded me of what people had said about Darts, "You can't take time to 'draw a breath.' "

Stitchers on different parts of the work all complained of the "bump" that came in the muscle on the right side of the back of the neck. It got "stiff" they said. One woman said she rubbed it every night when she got home and it helped some. She said she never got over having it feel that way. Some people mentioned a burning sensation. Other people complained of sometimes aching further down the spine. I noticed the knotting up of the muscle at the back of my neck and it reminded me of how it felt after playing the piano or typing for a long time. When tired or tense, this tightness would come much sooner.

The end of the day came at last. I entered in my diary,

Yesterday I learned the way to stitch darts and completed 13 pairs. Today I completed 88 pairs. The afternoon went better but I had some trouble with broken threads. I learned how to tell the "grain" by locating the place on the piece of cloth which corresponded to the unsewn one. My quota is *37 or 38 dozen pairs* of yokes per day to exceed base-rate pay per hour. My 7 plus dozen today leaves me a good way to go. . . . The new worker said she heard it was impossible to make money on the stitch dart job.

12. I Finish STITCHING

I STAYED ON STITCH DARTS FOR A FULL WEEK. While the day's routine was the same as the first two days (Thursday and Friday) and the work no different, I learned something new about the job and the situation every day.

SATURDAY

First thing Saturday morning Jeanie confided to me, "None of the top stitchers are in. That puts me in an awful fix."

Then the Service Girl came up and informed her in a gloomy voice, "I guess we'll have to pass out the black!"

I remembered how the girl in the washroom had said, "I hate to work on the black: that's the worst." Jeanie told me the black dye in the thread made it break easier.

The high school crowd were at work. More workers and more machines made more noise. A draggy sax number could hardly be heard as it wailed above the stitching. However, nothing dampened the gaiety of the high school girls. They whistled between pieces, especially after "I've Been Working on the Railroad" and "Anchors Aweigh." These numbers came over the best.

But no pieces cheered me. The white-haired machinist came by. He looked at me and said, "You'll like it better later." This steadied my shaky hands a bit. To get the kink out of the back of my neck I looked up at the ceiling, turned my neck, and straightened up in the chair. I didn't have to "leave the seat" to do any of this.

At 9:30 I went to the washroom. I stayed ten minutes. I thought I should eat my cookies when I was in the toilet to "save time." A THIN girl in the washroom was eating a peppermint pattie. She said, "I'm so tired."

A new FAT woman on our row said she had been changed from Lace. She said she was slow but that the work on lace didn't make her nervous.

As far as I was concerned, Saturday was "one of those days." I was glad I could leave at 11:45. Saturday's four-hour shift was long enough!

MONDAY

Several people were out when I arrived Monday morning. My FAT friend came in late—a little before 10:00. The high school girl next to me was out Friday and Saturday, and was late Monday. She said she had a funeral Friday, never came in on Saturday, and was kept at school Monday.

Irene came over with a bundle and I asked her if she had a good week end. She said, "No, terrible. Sunday morning, my head felt big as a barrel. Mother said, 'You don't feel up to going to church?' and I said, 'No.' I took a whole bottle of castor oil. It had peppermint flavoring and chocolate. I had a terrible cold and it's all gone today. I had an awful day yesterday but it's worth it. I'm all better today. I usually take magnesium citrate."

Later I asked Jeanie if she had had a good week end. "Oh, yes, fine!" she said and smiled. Jeanie had a husband and four children—two boys and two girls, the oldest thirteen. Her husband worked one block from home, which was a help. The children all went to school, as the youngest was seven. Jeanie didn't have to get to work herself until 10:00.

Irene was THINner than Jeanie, more nervous, less happy and well adjusted. Jeanie was more MUSCULAR, though not extreme. While she had less refinement of features, her appearance was more pleasing because of her goodhearted manner and general attitude towards life. I could see why Jeanie was the more popular supervisor.

However, the job was taking a lot out of Jeanie. She said her doctor told her she must have some recreation. She planned to go to Boston to hear the "Morning Breakfast Hour" at the studio where it was broadcast. She said that she could forget home while she was on the job, but that she was apt to carry home worries from work. She was getting nervous and restless. She couldn't *sit through* a movie any more. "It's too long," she said.

We were still working on black. My friend, the white-haired machinist, came by. He said cheerfully, "Oh, you're making slips for the nuns." His smile tried to encourage me. He also knew how people felt about the black. They all knew! As one supervisor said, "They [the workers] hate it. When they go fast hemming, the black thread breaks and gets all tangled up on the spool. They have a terrible time straightening it out."

After all I had heard about "the black," I was surprised I didn't have more trouble than I did; but I was glad to stop for lunch with FAT. She was always a cheering influence. She said I could have a room at her house. When I told her I'd bother her with my typing, she said they wouldn't mind.

Peg had a friend with her. FAT whispered to me that the friend was a "queer stick." She thought she held Peg back. She worked next to Peg, and Peg did her repair work. She had been "spoken to" for doing it. The friend was trying to get transferred to another mill where she wouldn't have to commute. She said she had to speak to the man in charge of personnel but she "hated like the devil" to do it! The job she wanted would be standing and Peg said she could never do a standing job.

FAT said to Peg's friend, "You've never felt the same since they changed the quota after you made it, have you?"

The friend replied, "No. I gave up."

FAT said time and again she'd just "make it" herself, and then they'd shift her to other work. She said, "It seems as though they don't want to *let* you get the piece rates!" Even when they did put her back on "Pinking," she had lost the former facility at it. "You lose the knack," she explained. Where she had done six dozen a day, she could do only three. "You have to work up skill again each time," she said. "You have to work *every minute* to make piece rates."

I was reminded of the girl who came to talk to the floor supervisor (forelady) the first day I visited the factory. The forelady had asked me to stay in to hear her story. The girl had been crying. She was upset over being shifted to another job of stitching. She said she had just learned the job well enough to get up to a little over the base rate an hour on the average and with the shift to new work it would cut her back.

The floor supervisor explained that after the learning period, she would have the opportunity to earn as much on the new job and that owing to lack of material the old work could not continue. She told me after the girl had left that they were trying to get girls trained who could shift from job to job and keep up their rates.

The afternoon work went better. I caught on to a trick of the motor speed. I ran it fast and then "let it die" so that the needle wasn't going too fast when it got off the cloth. This stopped the thread's breaking between pieces but didn't slow down the work too much. I could see there were "tricks to the trade."

The afternoon supervisor from the section in front of me stopped by. I asked, "How is everything?"

She said, *"Terrible.* They're all *waiting* for work and crabbing like the dickens." She was a pleasant-acting blonde—a MODERATE MIXTURE with some FAT emphasis.

However, for me, Monday had not been too bad a day—everything considered.

TUESDAY

Tuesday was "black" again, but the dark cloth didn't frighten me any more. I "regrained" two pieces from the previous day; then for an hour or more turned out a lot of black. I was going at good speed. I finished the bundle and was eager to push out more production.

But the next lot of material was *pink*. It was lighter weight than the black. I stitched too fast after working on the heavier black. The needle would run off fast and break the thread. I got the edge under the needle too and had to have a replacement. When I showed Jeanie the garbled cloth, she *wasn't* cross. She just said, "It happens sometimes."

Nevertheless this turn of events discouraged me when I had hoped to boost my output. The girls around me agreed that if everything was going wrong and you felt tired, it was better to rest a few minutes than to work. So I went to the washroom at ten and then to the Smoking Room. In all I was away from the machine *twenty* minutes!

I talked to two girls from Zig Zag who were in the Smoking Room. One said that the rate was easy, but that she guessed she was *too* ambitious. She pushed to make more all the time. She said the job didn't tire her. She guessed it was the housework. Her husband was in the army and her daughter thirteen in boarding school, but she had four rooms to take care of. She said, "The hardest thing is to write a letter every night."

A young girl complained of backache. She said she was out one day last week with lower back trouble. "Even after the war, we'll have to work," she sighed.

Finally I forced myself to go back to the "pink." I speeded up production a little but the thread still broke some. I was relieved when lunchtime came. FAT and Peg were cordial as ever. We ate together. FAT tried to give me courage. She said, "Try to add *just one or two over yesterday*. If you do that, it's good. It gets harder to improve each day."

As to herself, FAT said she was put on *Closed* Darts today just when she was getting near the quote on *Stitch* Darts. I had seen her make a wry face when she was given her work. "See, that's how it is," she went on, "I was getting almost up to my quote! I *hate Closed* Darts."

Peg said her friend didn't get a job at the plant near her home. Only "dirty" jobs were open, like bobbin cleaning. The friend decided to take a month off. "She *cries and can't stop*," Peg said.

FAT sympathized, "She's never been the same since they changed her quote on her. She's *discouraged.*"

As I looked back on my morning, I could understand. I thought I'd gotten the hang of the job, and then when the new material came and the thread began breaking all over again, I *felt* like crying myself. I was a little short on sleep and more easily discouraged than usual. Nevertheless it was *not* a good feeling.

In the afternoon I worked some more on pink, then later on white. The white went better than the pink. The thread was stronger and I had gotten back some of my speed. Each change, however, meant that I had to rethread the machine and then get used to the new thread and weight of cloth. This took time and held back production. At two o'clock, I went to the washroom and ate my cookies. The high school shift was just coming in.

I stopped in the Smoking Room for a few minutes on my way back from the washroom. A white-haired woman with a lovely face was there. She told me she'd been a stitcher twenty-five years and liked it. She was now on Straps. "This 'strap' job is *monotonous*," she said, "just *one* little operation. But it's not on piece rates and I'm glad it isn't. They've done a lot of time studies on it though. They may put a piece rate in later. There are so many in a bundle, it would be hard to count."

The girl sitting across from us volunteered, "Everyone knows there's lots of dissatisfaction on *Lace*. They've brought up people from downstairs and pay them more for the same work than the others get. Do you think *that's fair?* I'm not surprised the others don't like it. And they'll only be up a month and then go back down into war production."

The white-haired lady didn't want me to hear only complaints. She said sweetly, "This is the cleanest plant I've ever worked in. You should see some of the others. They have a fine hospital here too, and that's important."

I went back a bit revived. I pushed hard in the noise of the Victory shift. I didn't look up much. My eyes didn't feel tired but the back of my neck was stiff. To limber it up I looked at the ceiling several times and rotated my head. It "hurt" to do it.

I still felt discouraged about the output but the forelady for the whole floor came by. She smiled and congratulated me on my production for the day before. "Eleven dozen is good when you've never stitched before," she said. I took new hope and the white went well after that! By pushing I did a final half "bundle" (sixteen) which gave me ten more pieces than the day before. I remembered FAT's counsel and was satisfied to have kept up the rate and improved a little.

I checked "attentive" and "wide awake" on the score of subjective feelings I was noting morning and night. Often I'd check "bored," "inattentive," "sleepy," or even "strained and irritated" or "fatigued." But today I didn't feel discouraged at the end of the day. The neighbor to my right asked how I was doing. I said, "Not too bad."

WEDNESDAY

First thing in the morning, the nice "old man" came up behind me. He wanted to cheer me and put his hands on my shoulders. I jumped from surprise. He said, "I didn't mean to scare you—"

I worked a little and went to the washroom at nine. A woman there said you never got over getting a kink at the base of your neck. A girl said, "We should have a masseuse." The matron told how she used to go in to the nurse for "light" (lamp) treatments when her neck hurt after stitching.

I went back to work quickly hoping to increase production. I was buoyed up by yesterday's success and the talk of fatigue did not depress me. However the thread began to break again and the white cloth showed a lot of grease spots. I had to stop and clean them. I couldn't keep up the rate.

As usual, I had lunch with FAT and Peg. We saw Nettie (supervisor on Lace) in line. She said she never found the job boring. Every day just "flew by." She said any girl who didn't like it, it was because she wasn't interested and made up her mind she didn't like a job when she started to do it. She said there was no difficulty in making the quota.

When we got to the table, FAT and another woman said Nettie was smart and they didn't dislike her, but that she was speaking *for management* and not for the workers. As FAT said, "It's all right to say 'you don't get tired' when you're not the one sitting at the machine!"

FAT agreed that the most important reasons for fatigue were:
1. Change of work
2. Breaking threads, etc. (annoying hindrances)
3. Waiting for work.
"Those are the most important," she said.

In the afternoon, Jeanie came by. She said, *"Machine trouble is the worst. You know it's cutting down production and you can't help it."*

The woman next to me who had been transferred *back* to Darts had heard my conversation with Jeanie. She whispered to me later in the afternoon, "You know it's trying to 'make the quote' that tires you."

The end of the day came at last. My week on Darts was over. I felt I had learned a great deal besides how to stitch Darts. That took three weeks, I was told, and some jobs took four. When the girls in the washroom asked me if I was going to learn *all* the different jobs, I told them I thought I might talk to people who had done the other operations a long time and really knew them. I wouldn't have time to learn everything myself.

13. I Talk with the MANAGER

AFTER MAKING THE JOB SURVEY and getting reactions from veteran workers on different parts of the work, I felt I was ready to talk with the manager. I organized my ideas under ten headings.

Before looking at my ten suggestions, the manager knit his brows, "If I could only sleep nights—," he confided. "I didn't sleep a wink last night—just read."

I listened to Mr. Chase—to what he said and to what he didn't say. Nervous fatigue is no respecter of persons, and executives are people too. He was under stress. I realized I couldn't leave Mr. Chase out of the picture of his company.

He sincerely wanted to find the causes of nervous and mental strain among his workers. He was spending company money to find out. When I first talked to him, he said, "I'd like to know about the build-up of nervous tension with resultant *irritability*. What troubles the worker? If we can find out, it will help all stitchers."

I was trying to find out. I was finding out some things. I brought out the list. (I did not include problems of rate-setting. A new time study was then going on in the plant.) Under each heading was a brief statement of pertinent facts with a recommendation or query for further investigation. Items can be summed up as follows:

1. *Smoking Room*

The Smoking Room needed to be made more attractive and workers should be encouraged to rest and eat a snack in it ten minutes in the morning and afternoon. To create an atmosphere that would be both restful and diverting, I suggested putting plants in the windows and having a changing exhibit of paintings on the bare white wall.

2. *Sewing Machines, Tables, and Chairs*

One girl called my attention to the fact that when she sat close to the machine, it helped prevent backache. It took the strain off her middle and lower back as well as her neck. When the chair was further back she had to *lean forward* continually.

Existing equipment had some adjustment possible for tables and foot pedals. However, with the chairs nonadjustable, the range of possible distances suited some people but not others. I pointed out that if chairs, tables, and foot pedals were adjustable *with adequate range,* it should be possible to have equal comfort for *all* workers.

This would take care of "misfits" like the girl with a backache who told me, "I've tried it every way. The trouble is when I sit in close my feet are too far in front of the pedal. They slip off." This girl was large with long legs.

3. *Changing Focus to Rest Eyes*

Benefit from a restful view.

4. *Music and Noise*

Music programming must be timed and selected with reference to the amount of noise during different parts of the work day. Music programs were most effective during relatively quiet times. Saxophone numbers seemed to come over well during noisy periods. Also, loudspeaker coverage needed to be checked.

5. *Vibration and Noise*

Reduction of vibration would be a great help. Cushioning devices of rubber or suitable materials might be used on table and chairs.

A celotex-type ceiling would reduce noise. Also, screening the motor and noise-producing parts of the machines might be helpful.

6. *Sedentary Job with Enforced Lack of Change in Position*

Value to general circulation and relief of muscle tension when a chance to "get up and move around."

Spacing of rest periods for maximum benefit. Should there be a "set" time or should the individual take them when she feels the need or is at a good "stopping place"?

7. *Acute Problem in "Buckles" of Strap Section*

Should be investigated further. Nervous fatigue prevalent.

Some comments of workers:

"It makes you nervous trying to make the quote and if you don't, they won't keep you."

"It's working under pressure that makes you tired, and then *just sitting.*"

"The girl at the next table is out *for nerves.*"

"My eyes get tired. Then it's having to *hurry* all the time to make the quote."

8. *Possible Benefit of Gum-Chewing*

Might "comfort" worker and tend to help relieve tension. However, possible advantages probably more than offset by disadvantages of disposal problem and possibility of getting on materials.

9. *Importance of Service Girls and Supervisors*

Many comments emphasized this:

"When the work comes along and you are talked to nicely, you don't feel tired at the end of the day. Even if you are a little tired physically, you aren't tired mentally and you feel peppy to start the next day. But if someone bothers you on the job and you leave with something on your mind, you are tired before you start to work the next day."

The worker who made the above statement stressed the importance of having an *"agreeable"* working environment with people who knew how to be pleasant and tactful in handling the people who were under their supervision. She said, "Anyone over people should have studied psychology. They should know how to say things to people. I don't mind being corrected if it's done in the right way— if the person can be *nice* about it."

A good Service Girl is always prompt and pleasant and keeps the work coming along.

"In any job *unpleasantness* makes you tired faster than any amount of work."—"If you feel comfortable and happy where you work, you don't get tired."—"If the work comes along and everything is pleasant, you don't feel tired when night comes."

10. *Interviews with Workers As to What Bothers Them or What Helps Them*

Mr. Chase looked over the items on the sheets. He looked up at me with a warm smile. "That idea about pictures and plants is a 'pip,'" he said. He gave his consent to having a rotating exhibit of pictures installed in the Smoking Room.

Mr. Chase told me he had worked hard to get a Smoking Room in the first place. He meant workers to have rest periods and eat snacks in it. He said the ten-minute rest period in the Smoking Room applied to smokers and nonsmokers and that they could eat at this time if they wished. They could have sandwiches, milk, an apple, etc. Also people could go to the Smoking Room with their friends. He mentioned the case of two girls on the first floor who were inseparable—went to work, play, cafeteria, washroom, and Smoking Room together.

I told Mr. Chase the girls on the third floor had been eating in the washroom as they felt they would be criticized for doing it in the Smoking Room. We discussed the fact that apparently the supervisors did not understand the rest period, Smoking Room regulations. I said I hoped his policy could be clearly explained to supervision and the workers themselves.

Workers had made various comments in regard to supervisors' "rulings" as to use of the Smoking Room. One person told me, "Only one person from a department can go at a time. You can't go with a friend." Another said, "You can only ask permission to go *if you smoke.*" And one explained to me definitely, "You are *not* allowed *to eat* in the Smoking Room. One or two people have special permission to do it because of heart trouble or being especially faint after an early breakfast—and reasons like that."

I recalled Mr. Chase had told me that when rest periods had been tried before, they had always "degenerated"—probably due to "poor supervision." He looked at the list again and commented, "The majority of grievances seem to be concentrated around reaction to supervision. It's almost impossible to get adequately qualified supervisors. The girls here now earn far less than many of the stitchers, but they have about the hardest job in the plant. I guess we'll have to change to men who'll get higher pay—up to twice as much a week."

I couldn't help noticing the difference in the pay between men and women who were expected to do the identical job. I also offered the idea that *some* women supervisors seemed to be much better liked than others. I asked which kind he felt were most satisfactory. "For instance, how about Clara?" I asked. I had had many complaints about her.

"I know she's a *driver,*" he said quickly, "but she turns out the work. It's always of high quality." Then as if to defend his position, he added, "Workers who have been with her a long time don't want to be changed." I could see he liked this "kind" of supervisor.

On the other hand, when I mentioned Jeanie and how nice she was, he said, 'She's got to go. She's all done." He knew she was worn out nervously.

I remembered the washroom matron's comment about a popular male supervisor. "*Everyone* liked him," she said, "but they wouldn't keep him. He was *too nice*. They fired him. When he left, everyone who worked for him felt so bad they pitched in and gave him a present of fifty dollars."

Absenteeism was considered high and loss of employees large with no chance to get new ones. As Mr. Chase said, "It's not a question of getting *more* employees but of getting *more work out of the ones we have.*" Labor shortage was acute because of the war.

As to the absenteeism, Mr. Chase said, "I told the supervisors on Stitch Lace to tell the workers that they were sorry but since so many had been absent, it would be necessary to work *ten* hours a day this week." He added with feeling, "That ought to *show* them that absenteeism doesn't pay!" Apparently the good were punished with the bad.

When I asked Mr. Chase if the piece rate tended to encourage people to turn out less perfect work in order to make a higher total output, he said, "Oh, yes. A girl who can do a 100 will go to 140 with a lot of rejects."

I asked what he did in a case like that. "Oh, we throw all the repairs back at her and it holds her back so that she's back at the 100 rate. *Of course, this makes a disgruntled worker.*" He gave me a helpless, "baffled" look.

Mr. Chase wanted to find out what irritated workers and made them tired. He said I could have a series of interviews with workers in the fall and try to find out.

I left my conference with the manager both happy and sad. I was happy that I could improve the Smoking Room and bring in the interest of art exhibits. I was glad to have permission for interviews with workers. I was sad when I realized that flowers and music could not hope to be a panacea for problems of supervision.

Surely I must try to help *both* workers *and* management. Both areas must be relieved or a healthy organization could not result. The short-term plan was clear: arrange the art exhibits and make the improvements in the Smoking Room, then carry out the series of interviews with workers when the time seemed auspicious.

The long-range plan which might benefit management, and therefore the worker as a consequence, must wait until all the facts could be weighed together—until management could gain the over-all picture it sought: until it could see for itself why workers got tired, why they stayed away from work, why they sought work elsewhere.

14. WHAT CAN BE DONE?

I — THE SMOKING ROOM PROJECT
Pictures and Plants

THROUGH THE COOPERATION OF BARTLETT HAYES, director of the Addison Gallery of American Art at Phillips Academy, Andover, Massachusetts, the rotating art exhibits in the Smoking Room became a reality. He and I went to the plant one hot July day with the first exhibit.

Mr. Hayes had let me choose from the Addison Gallery's collection of oils the paintings which I felt would be of greatest refreshment to the workers. I had been guided in my selections by the subjects people had considered "pleasant" to think about when they took part in psychological experiments on reverie directed by Dr. Jacob E. Finesinger of the Psychiatric Department of the Massachusetts General Hospital in Boston.[5] For this hot day, I chose one

[5]Jacob E. Finesinger, M.D., "Effect of Pleasant and Unpleasant Ideas on Respiration in Psychoneurotic Patients," reprinted, with additions, from the *Archives of Neurology and Psychiatry,* XLII (September, 1939), 425-90. Copyright, 1939, by the American Medical Association.

painting of an *Ice Pond* and another *Snow Scene* of a house and trees in the snow. Other later pictures included ones of water, flowers, still life, and mother-and-child pictures.

All paintings were chosen with the purpose of pleasing and resting the worker. We wanted to give the worker relief from boredom, pleasant stimulation, and distraction from job irritations, and provide a change of focus to rest the eyes. Our efforts to counteract fatigue, heighten morale, and refresh the worker were in accordance with the psychological theory that "tiredness is correlated positively with unpleasantness."[6]

To add cheer to the Smoking Room, we set rosy-red geraniums in the windows with philodendrons for added green. The plants relieved the "fishbowl" feeling of the room. A thick linoleum floor covered the pitted cement. The new surface had quiet resilience which was pleasing to walk on and restful in effect. The red tile design went with the brick of the flower pots and suggested the atmosphere of an outdoor terrace.

The green wainscot blended well with the foliage, while the glaring white of the one windowless wall was now covered with ecru cloth as a background for pictures. There was ample space for two big paintings or for one large painting and two small ones. We could get quite a little variety in the different displays. Sometimes the small pictures were water colors or engravings instead of oils.

The series of exhibits consisted of nine periods of about two weeks each. The Addison Gallery provided pictures six times; twice some oils painted by a worker were displayed; and once, just before the last exhibit, we had a vacant period to see whether workers missed the pictures.

Comments of one worker when she saw us taking down the mother-and-child pictures reflect the general attitude of the majority

[6]"The Effect of Music on Feelings of Restfulness-Tiredness and Pleasantness-Unpleasantness," Department of Psychology, DePauw University; and the Radio Corporation of America. Published as a separate article and in the *Journal of Psychology*, XVII (1944), 299-318.

of workers. "We'll *miss* them," she said. "They make the room so 'homey.' It's so *restful* to come in here. It does something for you spiritually. I'm new here and I told my friends, 'Why, you should see the rest room. It has a beautiful big *hand painting* on the wall and windows all around with plants in them.' My friends could hardly believe it. They said, 'Why, no one does that.' I said, 'The management here is different. They're such nice people and good to work for.'

"It's worth the money to fix it up here and if you want, I'd be glad to 'speak up' about it. . . . This room is restful and even a few minutes here makes it so you can work better."

When I was at the plant in November, the washroom matron told me ten-minute rest periods had been put in both morning and afternoon and that eating in the Smoking Room was allowed. She said there wasn't any more eating or hanging around in the washroom. I wrote in my field diary:

As I passed by the Smoking Room there were groups of people in there eating and sitting around. One group with lunches and Thermos bottles were gathered in a circle around a low table. The green landscape painting and plants gave a pleasant atmosphere. The scene was in striking contrast to the barren, little-used room we saw last May.

II — INTERVIEWS
The Worker Speaks

I had seen, I had listened, I had worked—but that was not enough. What would the worker say when she had a chance to express her feelings?

At last, on November first, the interviews with workers which the manager had agreed to in our talk became a reality. At the request of the production manager, I was instructed to give the approved questionnaire personally, but *not* to ask any other specific questions. At the end of the questionnaire, I merely gave the worker a few minutes to make any comments she wanted to.

In many ways these spontaneous comments were more enlightening than directed discussion, for, in the selection of items she discussed, the worker revealed what was most important to *her*. I think the trend of a few representative workers from each of our body-type groups will be of interest. Let's listen to what different ones *chose* to say in this new situation.

Our setting was conducive to a feeling of ease and confidence on the part of the worker. I had found an unused storeroom on the second floor where we could talk in privacy and the worker could sit at a sewing machine. She felt at home in this situation and could demonstrate any aspects of the work which involved the work equipment. I had my chair drawn up close to hers.

I walked down with her from the workroom and as we arrived, I said, "The company said I could find a quiet place out of the way so this is our 'little home' out among the scraps." Days when it was a little cool in the big room, I would add, "It's a little cool, wouldn't you like to put on my coat?" I kept an extra one handy.

As I brought out the questionnaire, I remarked, "We hope this may help all people who do this kind of work. Even one or two things that help would be worth finding out."

Immediately after the worker left, I wote a few sentences which summed up the impression she made on me as a person and then checked a few observations as to her current physical and emotional tension and social attitudes.

Let's start with the one MUSCULAR-THIN and the two MUSCULAR women of the total fifty who volunteered.

MUSCULAR-THIN

Of the MUSCULAR-THIN I wrote:

This is a thin but forceful woman. She has a low, heavy voice and is poised and self-assertive in spite of tendency to a little tension. She has a good attitude and constructive ideas. Shows insight and understanding of this work and its problems.

She volunteered, "Now, I like to stitch. I've made my children's clothes and I like stitching. When I came to learn I knew what it was about, but some girls have never seen a machine before. That makes a difference.

"Then there's *interest*. Now some girls just come in because the pay is a little better than in the shoe shop or something and they're not interested in the stitching. They don't care if they learn it or not, or if they make the quote or not. They just want their money and that's all.

"Then there's the *rush* all the time. You're always trying to get out production. The quote is high. You're supposed to make it in three months but some girls don't. I don't know if it's the difference in the girl or the work or the machine. If you have to rip, it's bad. Just think how long a hem is. It holds you up. It's how the work comes to you. If it comes good you have a good day. If it runs bad, it's bad. We're the last operation on stitching.

"The thing is with rest periods, we know we can take them but on piece work you don't want to leave the machine. I go for a drink of water in summer and I get up once in a while. It gives your mind a change and rests your eyes. You've got to think of all those things."

MUSCULARS

Next I saw two MUSCULARS. I wrote of the first:

This is a highly MUSCULAR woman with some FAT. Even, moderately self-assertive temperament. Psychological callousness. Not sensitive. Spartan attitude towards work stress. Reactions of a strong person. Cooperative but independent. No anxiety or tension. This is an even, capable, strong worker with good work attitudes and no evidence of problems. Could stand stress.

It was evident from her answers to the questionnaire and her general attitude that she liked her work here and liked the situation, but she made *no* comments.

Of the second MUSCULAR, I said:

This worker has been with the company over two years. She is a pronounced MUSCULAR with a highly masculine appearance, but lacks the high aggression which often goes with this physique. Benign social conditioning is suggested by her ease of manner and open enthusiasm. When this worker was approached, she had just come back from the Smoking Room and was finishing eating something. She tackled her work with characteristic MUSCULAR energy.

She vouchsafed only one comment which was that she was "pretty well satisfied." Otherwise, like her fellow MUSCULAR, she had no comments on work or work conditions.

THINS

Comments of the typical THIN varied strikingly from the silence of the stoic MUSCULARS:

THIN said, "Well, you know, I'm the nervous type and I like the work, but it gets me awfully nervous. It's the changes, you know. They hold you back and I get awfully nervous. . . . My production drops. You know you just get up and going good, then a new style sets you back.

"Then it's how the work comes to you. Some of these new ones send up terrible work and that makes so many repairs. And when a lot of repairs come back it holds you up so. I'm slow at repairs anyway. I don't know what's the matter. When it got so bad I was all *nerved up* and I went to Mr. Traynor and said, 'I just can't keep on. I'll do *anything* else.' I thought I'd go crazy. But it's not so bad now. Two or three repairs a bundle isn't too bad. The work's going well now.

"You know you get twice as tired when the work doesn't go well and you get out half as much work. That's what makes you tired, is when the work doesn't go well. If it goes well you can do a lot and not feel half as tired. The machine couldn't be adjusted for the thickness of some of the seams. It would stop at the seam and not go over.

"It's my back that minds it. Right in the small of my back. Usually I don't notice it in the morning—perhaps a little around eleven o'clock, but I walk to the girls' room and it feels better when I get back. Then there's lunch, but around three o'clock I begin to mind it. I minded it a lot more on the nine hours a day. Of course some people just have a weak spot in their back. They mind it more; a lot of girls complain of it.

"I don't know whether it's the chair—whether it's too high or not. I tried a cushion for a while and it felt better. I guess a little change of position helps. But I like my work, I like Zig Zagging."

I wrote of this woman:

This is a typical THIN older woman—delicate, refined. Though not extreme, she has all the THIN earmarks. Her reaction to the work shows the nervous strain of this type. She is not a fast worker and is made nervous by changes, repairs, imperfect work coming to her. Gets backache, complains of *chair*. Tried cushion. Minds nine-hour day. Says backache worse when working nine hours.

No mention of problems of personal relations. This section seems to be very well handled and harmonious. THIN is a pleasant, sweet person, but minds nervous stress. Should not be subjected to more stress than can be helped. Might thrive better on day rate and with more frequent change of position. However is "making the grade" and can stand stress when work coming well.

Of another THIN, I wrote:

This is a quick-reacting ambitious THIN with a little MUSCULAR present. She has some "intellectual" tendencies. She is in distinct contrast to FAT who sits across the aisle from her. THIN *never* leaves her seat except to go to lunch. She is a high producer. Her youth and presence of some MUSCULAR development make her able to stand this work at this time and produce well. She appears well adjusted and not under personal emotional stress. However, this worker has a fairly high absentee record without explanation. (Check with medical records.)

I continued:

The picture of this girl suggests that she is one of the high producers who may show signs of nervous strain after a period of time or as life becomes filled with family cares. Her present adjustment and noticeable MUSCULAR component may carry her through with flying colors, but I should not recommend putting this girl in acute situations of social stress. Also, the fact that she *never leaves her seat* except for lunch is poor occupational hygiene. This means she gets no water or liquid, no change of position, no rest for eyes, and no psychological diversion.

This type of person is a "natural" producer under the wage-incentive system. She tends to be overambitious—a "compulsive" worker to some extent—and will make "the sky the limit" as a piece-work goal. How long this sort of activity can be maintained depends on a number of factors both in the work situation and personal life.

Social conditions in this plant are very benign to this type of a person. She would not thrive on "being hollered at."

When I checked with the medical records, two facts stared me in the face: *slightly enlarged thyroid, rapid pulse.* They had also noted thin stature, underweight, slight acne on face. I felt less optimistic than ever about this girl's endurance in this kind of work.

I found the third THIN had a heart murmur. The last THIN was in no way extreme and almost fell in the MODERATE MIXTURE group. Of her, I said:

She has the quick reaction of a THIN, with good intelligence, but she seems to be far less apprehensive, compulsive, tense than the other THIN high performers. She is more sociable. . . . Appears to be a well-adjusted high performer.

Her medical record pointed out the fact that she was undernourished, but she had no major physical infirmity.

It was very obvious to me that an extreme THIN reacted quite differently from one with added MUSCLE or MODERATE tendencies. I felt that, in generalizing about the suitability of THINS for particular jobs, great care would have to be used in noting the presence of secondary trends which might sway the balance and indicate a highly satisfactory worker for a given job. However, for long-term performance at stitching, it appeared that *extreme* THINS would not be the best bets, even though they might be high performers for a time.

Muscular tendencies *added to* thin made a great difference, as we have seen from the first muscular-thin example and the thin woman with some muscular development. Apparently the stoicism of the extreme muscular helped to counteract the sensitivity of thinness. We remember how the musculars had *no* complaints. Also the matter-of-fact muscular-thin mentioned the problem of repairs and "how the work comes to you" without the emotionalism of the typical thin.

Plump-delicates

I wondered what would happen to thin tendencies when fat was added. Two plump-delicates combined these two trends. Of the first, I wrote:

This woman is short—five feet. Also her body is short in relation to her legs. She has the plumpness of an older woman but suggests the fragility of youth. She likes her work but gets backache, pain in chest, cramps in legs, and swelling of ankles due to lack of comfortable chair height or adjustability of work equipment. Has home anxiety of daughter with five children under seven years; the daughter's husband "volunteered" for war. Well adjusted to social environment, likes supervisors, clean plant, etc. Tolerant toward younger workers. *Only* problem is one of mechanical requirements of body build in relation to work equipment.

She said, "I like the work. It's nice here. It's so clean too. The *only* thing is the chair. I'm short and my legs are long. When the chair is high, my legs are up and my back has to stoop over. It aches across my shoulders [trapezius muscles] from pushing through the cloth [uses both hands on stitch yoke—has larger pieces of material than some other processes.] After a while it gets me in the back and across the back of my shoulders. When I straighten up, it pains in front [puts hand on bottom of sternum]. I notice it here especially after eating. My legs are long and they are up, so the blood doesn't circulate. I get cramps in the backs of my legs and my ankles swell. [Note: Nurse mentioned prevalence of swollen ankles.] The *only* thing is the chair. I like the work and I like the supervisors. They're so nice.

"I never go to the Smoking Room. I don't smoke and they'd just think I was in there listening. . . . I go to the 'sink room' two or three times in the morning and two or three times in the afternoon. I said to Frances, 'Sometimes I get so tired.' She said, 'When you feel like that, get up and take a little walk. Go to the washroom or get a drink.' I do that now and it makes me feel better to stand up and move around. I feel lots better when I get back."

Of the other PLUMP-DELICATE, I wrote:

This is a nervous high-keyed, conscientious worker. Been here over two years. A likable Irish spinster who had to earn her own living and has worked hard all her life. She lives alone but makes the best of it. Has supper with her sister often. Fond of nephew. Has her friends in.

As she said, "I try hard. I'm not like the married women here who *don't care* if they lose their jobs. I have to work and I always will. I don't mind it at home evenings. I fix my supper and wash out underwear and do things around the house. It's a nice change after sitting down all day. Then I read the paper and it's time to go to bed."

A number of her comments suggested PLUMP (FAT) good-natured understanding and tolerance of people. Her remarks on supervision were made without undue emotionality. She said,

"Lots of girls left. Thought they could do better somewhere else. Just dissatisfied.

"Everyone wants the good ones [supervisors], but you have to go where they send you. Sometimes the work keeps up a long time but other times there's not so much and it changes fast. I'll tell you, the main thing on the job is the supervisor. There's an awful difference in supervisors. Now, Virginia that I had for over a year was wonderful. She'd always encourage the girls. She'd never *throw back repairs* at them or criticize them. If you got discouraged, she'd come and talk to you. *She'd do the repairs herself* even if it wasn't her job. She didn't want to discourage the girls. Then the way she'd talk. Everyone "felt somehow" about Virginia, and everyone's glad she got the promotion. She deserves it. She always worked hard.

"There's such a difference when a supervisor is *considerate* and talks to you in a decent way. You appreciate it. That's the most important thing in this factory. When a supervisor *bosses 'em* or *dogs 'em,* they just feel terrible. The forelady jumps on anyone who does, but she can't be everywhere all the time. Stasia's good too. If anything comes up, you can always talk it out with Stasia and she fixes it up. Lorraine's nice too [present supervisor], but she's young and of course she has a lot to learn. She's nice, though."

However, in spite of PLUMP-DELICATE's ease in talking and tolerance for people, parts of her conversation were reminiscent of the typical THIN woman above. For instance, her first remarks were:

"I hate to get back repairs. Some people don't mind though. They just take them and do them. They don't seem to pay any attention. It makes me feel terrible though."

Later she said:

"I've got a cold inside today and I don't feel so good. Everything's going bad. I got within four of the quote this morning; then they changed us this afternoon and I don't feel so good. I'm discouraged. I hope they don't *speak to me* tonight about how poorly I've done. They never *have* spoken to me. They just say 'Do the best you can,' but I never know. I feel so bad *inside* [puts hand to heart] when things don't go well and I'm not up to the quota.

"I never take time out and I don't hang around the 'sink room' the way some girls do. I just go there once in the morning and once in the afternoon. That's all. I feel I want to be doing all I can. I've never been on piece rate before. I was always day rate. It's just that I feel *rushed.* I don't notice it while I'm working on my *nerve,* but I *feel it* when I stop. The trouble with me is I look at the work I've done because I want it to be all right. I don't want it to come back. They [the supervisors] say I should just let it slide through and let the inspectors do that. But I can't help it. They think I'd work faster if I didn't look it over, but I used to be on samples and we always thought it was such a shame when work came back wrong."

While some FAT may have eased life here and there for the PLUMP-DELICATES—particularly in their relations with people—they still appear far from ideal to take the stress of a job like stitching. The DELICATE (THIN) tendencies make some aspects of the job harder to take. Compulsive feelings and tension tend to creep in.

After all, all the types we have discussed so far were "minority groups" among the fifty stitchers. The three remaining types made up over *four-fifths* of the workers interviewed. Therefore these types—FATS, MUSCULAR-FATS, and MODERATE MIXTURES—are of crucial interest. Are they different from the other four types in their reactions to the work? How do *they* feel? What do *they* say? For instance,

TYPICAL FATS

While many of the thirteen FATS had a little muscular development, they were strikingly different in reaction from the full-fledged *MUSCULAR*-FATS. For instance, three times as many FATS as MUSCULAR-FATS were *discouraged*. A glance at a few FATS *will* bring out comparisons with the MUSCULAR-FATS to follow.

Of one twenty-five-year-old FAT, I wrote:

This is a typical FAT—now not extreme but will probably become more so. Slow reaction and lack of high drive. Sociability and not liking to have to "sit there and keep your eye right on it" (the work) makes this worker a frequent user of the Smoking Room. "I'm always in there," she said. She also shows a high absenteeism record. Lack of MUSCULAR characteristics may account for the comment, "the work is *hard*," and lowered drive does not "keep her at it." However, she can do the work when she tries, as her record shows. She gives no evidence of minding the nervous stress. No question of "strain." She "rests" or is absent and does not let herself work under "tension."

Of another I said:

High FAT (small hands, etc.), pleasant, soft-voiced girl. Goes to Smoking Room. Sociable. Not high producer. High absenteeism. Health appears good although "sick" frequently on record. Suggests FAT sociability, etc., without high drive. Production curve varies. Repair problem.

And about a third:

Plump, strong young girl. FAT definitely dominant. Easy, pleasant FAT manner. High absentee record and moderate performance suggest FAT reaction to this work. Uses Smoking Room. Sociability of this type person evident.

Muscular-fats

Muscular-fats are of such interest to later analysis, I think it will be worth while to list comments of all eight. The major emphases of MUSCULAR-FATS will be clear. They showed a certain amount of independence and self-assertion. Many had ideas and made constructive suggestions—particularly "number eight." With two exceptions (one of discouragement and one of resentment), all eight MUSCULAR-FATS showed *no* evidence of anxiety, tension, resentment, or discouragement as noticed for a good many other workers. In general, they were *workers who LIKED to work.* There were few complaints and almost no emotionalism in regard to the job.

Of the first MUSCULAR-FAT I wrote:

Young, energetic MUSCULAR-FAT. Loves sports. Would like noon dancing and evening competitive sports with other mill teams. Well adjusted, young, vigorous. Pride in company. Good employee material. Enough MUSCULAR to welcome *activity* after sedentary work. Important for strong, young workers.

She said, "You know, a lot of the young girls don't have anything to do at night and they hang around the streets. If they had a game one night a week with some other mill team, it would be good. You know, the people at the rubber company ask me what's the matter—why we don't have a team at Textron. You know, we'd feel proud to talk about the Textron team and it would put Textron on the map.

"Basketball in the winter or softball or volleyball or baseball—anything like that in summer. Girls could practice half an hour after work on an open lot nearby, and our bus doesn't come 'til 5:30. Then some might want to come over for a half-hour on Saturdays. A lot of girls would like it, but you feel funny to walk up to the front office and say you want to play softball."

Of "number two," I said:

Typical MUSCULAR-FAT. Fat on hips—muscular legs. Some texture in face, however. This girl has been with the company over two years. Came when company started. Shows drive and self-assertion. Immediately asked *why* I was asking the questions (on questionnaire)—but soft FAT voice, pleasant manner, and FAT sociability. Says health of self and whole family is excellent. (Note: Was out yesterday. Evidently *not sick* but did not find reason. High absenteeism not explained.) This is a capable worker. Has adjusted to many changes and evidently can stand social or physical stress well. Would work out well seated beside MUSCULAR. Competence of MUSCULAR no threat to this worker. Social adjustment evident here. However, she made *no comments*.

"Number three":

This is a typical Greek MUSCULAR-FAT—a fine, strong, plumpish girl with a strong face but pleasing manner. She likes the work and has no complaints. (Note: Absences for this girl seem surprisingly high.) Could stand stress. This girl is in sharp contrast to a new girl who sits beside her. The new girl does not have the drive, build, or personality, and is *not* typical of the majority of successful stitchers who stay on the job year in and year out.

"Three" stated her position briefly, "I like it here. It's so nice. It's so clean. I'd never leave to work anywhere else—in any other factory, I mean. I've worked in others and this is the best factory here. I'd never leave unless for a better job. I'd never change for a different factory. I like the work."

Of "number four," I wrote:

This is a typical MUSCULAR-FAT. All teeth out and sick recently, but, has "Spartan indifference" of MUSCULAR. No complaints. Not a high producer, but with improved health looks like a type to stick at this kind of work.

Her comment reminded me of the MUSCULARS. She said, "I like the work, that's all."

Of "number five":

This is a powerful MUSCULAR-FAT with THIN legs and fingers. FAT predominates in the temperament, and a certain gynandro-morphic (masculine) tendency is present. She is a competent, satis-fied worker. Stands stress well.

"Five" had more to say. She talked about the work: "The thing is it's harder to make good on the satin. The crepe paid much better. Some of the girls have trouble getting up to the quote.

"I like the job [pinking]. I like it better than Zig Zag. . . . Zig Zag's too slow. The needle goes back and forth so many times to the inch. Pinking goes straight and you can turn it out faster.

"Some of the girls have a backache at first but that wears off—at least mine did. You don't hear the girls talk about it much, but the new ones complain about it. Of course, I will say you really *work*.

"The company does 'everything' for us. It's swell that way. And everyone's so nice. They're pleasant to be with.

"The main thing is the satin. I like crepe better. Satin's much harder to handle. They always start girls on crepe."

"Number six":

This is a massive MUSCULAR-FAT with a strong, rugged face and build. However, though moderately self-assertive, she has a soft voice, FAT amiability, and a sense of humor. She has worked on many jobs during her two years with the company. She is a steady worker and likes to give the job all she's got. "When I work, I like to work," she says. She never leaves her seat except for lunch. Goes to the Ladies' Room only at lunchtime.

"Six" was the only MUSCULAR-FAT who showed discouragement. She said, "Changes bother. You just get up to your quote and then there's a change. I just got to making the lace and straps and then there isn't any more.

"You get *nervous* when you're afraid you're not going to make the quote. Anyway I get my rate."

I noted after her spontaneous comments:

Note: This is a rugged, powerful woman; but even with her, *changes* are discouraging and fear of not making the "quote" makes her *nervous*. This worker is a typical MUSCULAR-FAT with vigor and low anxiety tendency. She could stand a good deal of stress and has enough FAT to mellow her MUSCULAR aggression and restlessness.

And, next-to-last, "number seven":

This is a typical MUSCULAR-FAT. Self-assertion and attitude to supervision has an "active," but constructive, quality. She appreciates good aspects of the work situation. There is no physical or nervous emphasis in her comments; "executive" problems interest her as they do "number eight." Before the questionnaire began, "seven" made a number of appreciative comments to me on the company and management policies. However, she was the one of the eight to show a trace of resentment in her attitude. She had only one suggestion to make. It was a reasonable, carefully considered comment.

She said, "It's just about the supervisors. Not any special one, but it seems as though the supervisor should *know* the job she's over. She should work on it at least four weeks so she'd understand it. . . . Often the Service Girl knows the job better than the supervisor. They just pick out a girl and put her in charge whether she's ever done *that* work before or not."

And last, I wrote of "number eight":

This is a typical pronounced MUSCULAR-FAT. Drive and self-assertion of MUSCULAR, but sociability and interest-in-people like FATS. Good worker. Absences due to housework interest—not healthy, strong person. Intelligent worker with job and social insight. Has been asked to be supervisor, but says she is nervous about *showing* people. Would favor conscientious worker even if slow, but not have patience with a worker who wasn't doing her best and would "tell her so." Insight into own MUSCULAR characteristics. Not want to be a supervisor. However, think would do well. MUSCULAR-FAT *executive* type. *Ideas. Social values.*

The way "eight" tackled problems shows why management wanted her for a supervisor. She began, "The thing I'd like to say about the trouble with the machinists is: You ask and ask for them and nothing happens. Last week my machine was sticking and I asked to have it fixed. I know the 'feel' of the machine and I *knew* that was the trouble. But no one came and I could make only seventy dozen. This week it finally got fixed and I made ninety dozen. It would've helped everybody if it had been fixed when I asked for it.

"It's the same with the other girls. They ask, and Agnes doesn't put on the light. I can see how she feels; she wants to wait and give it a chance to 'work out.' If it's a new girl I understand, but with us who've been here a long time, we don't ask until *after* we've tried a new needle and checked the tension and pressure. Two girls left because they couldn't ever get the machines fixed. It was a *daily* altercation and they just got sick of it.

"Like when we have a new style. Style #25 takes a different foot from the one we were doing before, and we'd been on them four weeks before they put on the other foot. It held down production and it made more repairs. We were working *blind* and we couldn't help making mistakes. You couldn't go over but one stitch and you couldn't see. When there get to be so many repairs, 'they' finally look into it. *We* could tell them *why* we make the mistakes. I say 'an ounce of prevention' is best. It's better all 'round. There's more production and the girls feel better about the work.

"And when you couldn't see with the closed foot, you had to twist your neck around to peek under, and it gave you a kink in the neck and you couldn't work so fast.

"Another thing, if they'd let you know *how many* they want put out. At the beginning of the day if Agnes said to the girls, 'Do you think we can get out so many—fifteen, eighteen, or twenty dozen—today? We need so many dozen today,' the girls would try to get them out. They'd do it *for* her. As it is now, we're just *working blind.*

"If they'd *ask* the girls to do things instead of *telling* them, I know it would work much better.

"Another thing, about *talking.* Now there's quite a little to that. Take in the morning, we all like to talk the first hour before we're *settled down.* If Agnes noticed, by nine we're all settled down to work. The only time I talk is when *I have to to relax me.*

"Now it's different with different people. The girl next to me likes to talk *all the time.* She's got a reputation for it with all the supervisors, but she *works better that way.* It doesn't bother me either. We tried an experiment on it, and I was seventy when the machine was sticking and ninety when it was fixed, but she talked to me all the time. It wasn't the talking that bothered me. If I think it's bothering the work at all I just say, 'Can it, will you? I can't work.' She doesn't mind. The lady on the other side is old. She doesn't mind it; she doesn't pay attention. The talk is all directed at me, anyway.

"There's just a difference in temperament. If the supervisors realized that, it would be better. Now I don't mind listening, but I couldn't talk all the time *myself* and turn out the work. The thing is if a girl is a conscientious worker, she is trying to turn out the work and do her best. Of course, some girls just talk and fool around and don't try; well, they deserve to be spoken to. But if the supervisors stop to think, they can tell who's trying.

"Anyway, you know *if you tell people not to do a thing, they want to do it just that much more.* If the supervisor just said, 'We've got so much work we've got to do today; can we do it?' the girls would pitch in. They *pick at us* a lot for talking. If they realized a conscientious worker just does it to *relax,* it would be a help.

"Now, as to change, people are different. They have different temperaments. With me I don't mind a change. After I've been on a style two weeks I'm *glad* to change. But some people hate to change and it makes them very nervous.

"Another thing, I say if I can do eighteen dozen *every* day, it's better than to *push* for twenty and then only be able to do fourteen dozen the next day. I say let a person take her own speed. It's better for everyone in the long run.

"I never use the Smoking Room; I don't smoke. I only leave *when the work is going badly* and I have to *get away from the machine.* I just go to the Ladies' Room once or twice a day and never over ten minutes. What I do is to come back a little *after* the lunch bell. But I figure I've got ten minutes sometime and I'd rather take it then.

"The eight-hour day is fine, but I do hope this *overtime* stops. Nine hours a day and four hours on Saturday is too much. Of course it's not so bad for the single girls. They like to get the money, but I have a home and I like to clean it Saturday.

"Mary is grand. She divides the work evenly and tries to give people the work they like. I take it as it comes but some people are hoggish and want the work that pays more. One style now pays two-and-a-half cents more than another.

"Agnes is nice too [supervisor]. She's open and frank and doesn't beat around the bush.

"Sometimes I think of leaving, but then I think it's *pleasant* here. It's clean. And they always are *trying to make it better.* It's *how people act on each other, too.* That's the whole thing in a place. I've worked other places and I know. It's the temperament in a place.

"If they'd tell you *why* it's important to do a thing a certain way, we'd try hard to do it that way. The supervisors must know *why* it *has* to be a certain way and *if they'd tell us,* it would *help a lot.* Take the width of the seam for instance. I like to stitch close to the edge; well, the forelady came and explained to me how it has to be one-eighth of an inch *in* because they cut it along the edge and if I stitch close they can't do it. I can see how it is, and I worked awful hard for two weeks to break myself of the habit of stitching close to the edge. When you *know why,* you don't mind; but if they just say *do this* and *do that,* you don't see why it isn't just as good the way you've been doing it."

While "number eight" had a great deal to say, it is of interest to compare the trend of her remarks with those of the typical THIN above. Several points are the same, but MUSCULAR-FAT's reaction and approach to solutions of problems differ from the personalized emotion of THIN.

"Eight's" conversation also presents quite a striking contrast to the sociable easy talk of FATS, which did not contain a wealth of ideas and constructive suggestions. The comments of MUSCULAR-THIN seem nearest to "eight's" trend, but it may be recalled that MUSCULAR-THIN showed signs of tension. No MUSCULAR-FAT appeared tense.

In looking at the MUSCULAR-FATS as a group, it is apparent that several tended in the direction of MUSCULAR "silence," while the rest exhibited varying degrees of FAT talkativeness. However, where FATS used their conversational powers for purposes of sociability, *MUSCULAR*-FATS talked often about *work*. All in all, the MUSCULAR-FATS left one with the impression of job "veterans." Examination of their production and employment records will be of interest when compared with others of the seven groups.

MODERATE MIXTURES

By definition MODERATE MIXTURES included people of mingled tendencies. There were many of this relatively balanced type. *Perfectly* balanced MODERATE MIXTURES, Sheldon's "ideal," showed evidences of all three trends with none predominant. However, many MIXTURES were of the imperfectly balanced variety.

In going over comments, it became apparent that where, in the combination of tendencies, one emphasis—as FAT, MUSCULAR, or THIN—had a decided edge over the other two kinds of traits, reactions were more nearly similar to that type. Where two trends were present to a noticeably greater degree than the third, reactions moved in the direction of a combined type. For instance, if MUSCULAR and FAT were predominant over THIN, people leaned towards reactions of MUSCULAR-FATS.

While none of these single or combined predominances were sufficient to move the person into the pronounced type itself, individuals appeared and acted like the "borderline" MIXTURES that they were. However, the fact that they were only "MODERATE" MIXTURES meant that no trend was extreme of its kind.

15. Let's Compare STITCHERS

SURVIVAL OF THE FITTEST

WHO SURVIVED STITCHING BEST of the "types" we have talked to? I'll bet you can guess. (Table 14.) *All* the MUSCULAR-FATS and the two MUSCULARS! They had taken jobs when the company was just getting under way two years before and had remained on their jobs. They were 100 per cent "veterans" in fact.

No other body type had *all* two-year veterans, but more than half of the MODERATE MIXTURES and nearly half of the FATS had been with the company either two years or one year or more. By definition I called all workers who had lasted a year "veterans."

The lone MUSCULAR-THIN, all four THINS, and one PLUMP-DELICATE (of two) were also veterans. It is of interest that these three *rare* types of veterans all had THIN characteristics as one of their dominant tendencies. While PLUMP-DELICATES and MUSCULAR-THINS (as well as MUSCULARS) are not common types among women (p. 12), THINS themselves are not hard to find. Where were they? It looked as though people who were noticeably THIN either were

TABLE 14

Length of Service

	Veterans	Recent	New
Fat	22222211111 (22%)	R (2%)	N (2%)
Muscular-fat	22222222 (16%)		
Muscular	22 (4%)		
Muscular-thin	1 (2%)		
Thin	2111 (8%)		
Plump-delicate	2 (2%)	R (2%)	
Moderate mixture	2222222221111 (26%)	R (2%)	NNNNNN (12%)

Note: Each symbol represents one person; per cents refer to the percentage of the total group of fifty.

Key: 2 means 2 years or more.   R means recent, 6-11 months.
      1 means 1 year or more.   N means new, 1 month.

not likely to survive at the work or did not choose or were not chosen to stitch.

While it would seem that most personnel experts would have become aware of this, such did not seem to be the case—especially in times of scarce labor. I saw a group of new stitchers on one visit. I noted many unfavorable types among them. On my next visit quite a while later, the person I had talked with before said, "Do you remember that group we were training last time you were up? They've almost all *left!*" Needless to say, even with a labor shortage to contend with, a policy of hiring people regardless of type had cost the company effort and money; and it must have been discouraging to the workers themselves.

I want to hasten to point out that for some other types of work, THIN traits are often great assets and may be major requisites for competence; but for an arduous, wearing job like stitching, THIN assets do not appear to meet the major requirements of the work.

I think these "facts" make sense to us after having become acquainted with stitchers and having heard what they had to say. It became clear that different types of people reacted differently to the same job. As you recall, one supervisor had said, "THIN girls are nervous. They cry if the thread breaks twice."

HIGH PRODUCERS—LOW PRODUCERS

After studying over the company's records and standards for average performance, I listed the production of workers interviewed as to *high, average,* and *low* production. I included all but eight women (the seven new workers and one FAT V-1 on day rate). Of the rest, five were *low,* twenty-one were *average,* and sixteen were *high* producers.

High Producers

All high producers were veterans. Over 80 per cent had been with the company two years or more.

However, *not all veterans* were in the group of high producers. In the high production group were:

nearly two-thirds (62½ per cent) of the MUSCULAR-FAT veterans;
over one-third (36 per cent) of the MODERATE MIXTURE veterans;
about a quarter (27 per cent) of the FAT veterans.

Of types scarce in our sample, I found among high producers one of the two MUSCULAR veterans and two of the four THIN veterans.

From the point of view of availability and suitability for stitching, MUSCULAR-FATS seemed to take the prize. They could perform and endure; and there exist a reasonable number of them. On this basis, MODERATE MIXTURES would place second and FATS third.

Low Producers

Of the five low producers, there were *no* MUSCULAR-FATS, MUS-CULARS, or MUSCULAR-THINS.

One recent MODERATE MIXTURE (nine months) and one recent FAT (seven months) were low producers. Obviously, they were *not* veterans.

On the other hand, not only were *both* PLUMP-DELICATES low producers, but one was a two-year veteran and the other, eleven months on the job. The one THIN who was a low producer was also a veteran (V-1). Therefore "time" (that is, practice) had not turned these PLUMP-DELICATES and this THIN into satisfactory performers.

NATIONAL EXTRACTION

The company doctor's comments were still in my mind. "French and Greeks make good stitchers," he had said. "Irish and Polish are better for heavier work."

I looked eagerly at the high producers to see which nationalities out of those in the sample fifty had "made the grade." The doctor would not be surprised to find that all the workers of Greek extraction were high producers, as were nearly half of all French-Canadian strains. Only one Polish worker of four was a high producer. In the interview she volunteered, "I liked the war work. It was heavier."

It may be of even greater interest to learn that not a fraction but *all* the French-Canadian and Greek MUSCULAR-FATS were high producers, whereas *only one out of five* French-Canadian FATS was a high producer. This situation suggests that people of less-favored builds in the same nationality may *not* be as successful at the work.

I thought a look at the nationalities of low producers might shed a little light on the subject. I found two French Canadians among the low producers. However, neither of these women had a pronounced MUSCULAR trend alone or in combination: they were THIN and PLUMP-DELICATE. You may recall there were *no* MUSCULARS, MUSCULAR-FATS, or MUSCULAR-THINS in the low-producing group. The *type* of person who was a low performer appeared to be more decisive as to performance than whether she was of French extraction or not.

"GOOD BETS" FOR STITCHERS

The problem of selection of "good bets" for stitchers, according to this sample, looks like an easy task for the personnel "selector."

It looks as though he wouldn't go far wrong if he first grabbed every MUSCULAR-FAT that applied. He also would probably not make much of a mistake to take the few MUSCULARS and MUSCULAR-THINS who might come his way. Then, as MODERATE MIXTURES and FATS were "survivors" in this work, he need only steer away from extreme THINS and the rare PLUMP-DELICATES.

PART IV - UNDER THE MICROSCOPE

(Research at Harvard Fatigue Laboratory)

IN THE LABORATORY

WHILE IT IS IMPOSSIBLE to put a "person-as-a-whole" under a microscope, it is not impossible to subject individuals to laboratory tests in order to see how different people respond to the same laboratory situations. We have become acquainted with different types of people in action on their jobs. Now it will be interesting to see how typical examples react to laboratory tests. For instance, does a MUSCULAR-FAT vary from a THIN or a PLUMP-DELICATE when the scientist makes him (or her) jump through laboratory "hoops"?

Naturally, I was delighted when the lab okayed an exploratory study of individual differences in nervous and mental fatigue. While this was a small pilot study, it involved the *whole* person, as well as *the test*. At this stage the objective was not to work with large numbers but to *know* each subject and see him in similar and different situations over a long period of time.

In all, we studied twenty-five people. We tried to find some extreme types for purposes of comparison. We used both men and women. Four college men were studied in a preliminary trial of testing methods and fourteen more were added later as subjects for

113

the experiments. Seven women in sedentary jobs completed the series. The college men were seen over one or two college terms, with appointments scheduled for twice a week. The women were seen twice a week for several months and casually for about a year.

I shall not go into details of the experimental "red tape," but discuss the findings on examples of types already familiar to us from what we have read so far. For instance, we'd all like to know about MUSCULAR-FATS. Are they as good as they're cracked up to be? Can they stand being laboratory guinea pigs? And then how about those THINS! We shall discuss these and other examples under two headings: Subjects Are People and What Does a Test Test?—or to put it bluntly—*DIFFERENT people take tests.*

16. Subjects Are PEOPLE

LET'S LOOK AT A FEW MEN

FOR THE COLLEGE MEN, I had medical and psychological findings already gotten by experts in the Hygiene Department. I think you may like to see the way these subjects impressed people who had no contact with the laboratory research, and who had no particular concern with body types as we are defining them. I did not even look at these records until after every laboratory test was taken and every observation made.

For instance, let's make clusters of the adjectives which were checked on five personality summaries (Figure 5).[7] The men who gained these impressions of our subjects were making judgments in the light of comparisons with hundreds of college men who went

---

[7]William L. Woods, M.D.; Lucien Brouha, M.D.; Carl C. Seltzer, Ph.D.; in collaboration with Clark W. Heath, M.D.; Arlie V. Bock, M.D., Dr. Phil.; John M. Flumerfelt, M.D.; and Frederic L. Wells, Ph.D., *Selection of Officer Candidates,* Studies in the Relation of Personality to Field of Work, from The Grant Study, Department of Hygiene, Harvard University (1943). Harvard University Press, Cambridge, Mass. London: Humphrey Milford. Oxford University Press.

Muscular-fat		Thin	
Energy	Relaxed	Energy	Self-conscious
Strong	Even	Excitable	Shy
Steady	Warm	Erratic	Sensitive
Stable	Bland	Changeable	Spontaneous
Dependable	Contented		
Controlled	*Friendly*	*Controlled*	
Adaptable	*Natural*	*Adaptable*	
Cooperative		*Cooperative*	

Moderate mixture

No traits pronounced except

Friendly
Cooperative

Muscular		Muscular-thin	
Initiative	Leader	Independent	
Energy	Even	Poised	Asocial
Poised	Warm	Steady	
Steady	Bland	Dependable	
Stable	Contented		
Dependable	Spontaneous		
Controlled	*Friendly*	*Controlled*	
Adaptable	*Natural*	*Adaptable*	
Cooperative			

Fig. 5 — Brief personality summaries

through their examinations. Body type has been added here by taking the type from the Fatigue Laboratory studies of these same individuals.

It will be noted, among other things, that while MUSCULAR-FAT, MUSCULAR, and THIN, all have *Energy,* and are *Adaptable, Controlled,* and *Cooperative,* THIN is not *Friendly* or *Natural.*

It will be noted that while MUSCULAR-FAT, MUSCULAR, and THIN, all give evidence of *Energy,* THIN appears to use his energy in a different way from MUSCULAR and MUSCULAR-FAT. That THIN is *Erratic, Excitable,* and *Changeable* as compared with the other two types makes an important difference in the use of his energy.

It will be noticed that in MUSCULAR-THIN, MUSCULAR tendencies cancel out marked THIN tendencies that we see predominantly present in THIN. However, as compared with MODERATE MIXTURE and with the other three types, MUSCULAR-THIN alone lacks both *Friendly* and *Cooperative* tendencies. MUSCULAR-THIN's *Asocial* and *Independent* traits take him in the other direction.

In a final summary of personality with reference to Appearance, Expression, and Speech, we find the following assortments of traits checked as noticeably present (Figure 6) for the same five subjects. All traits were medium for MUSCULAR-THIN.

In glancing at the Appearance, Expression, and Speech summaries, it appears that while MUSCULAR and THIN are both *Animated* and *Alert,* they are animated and alert in different ways. THIN is weak and tense about his animation: MUSCULAR is strong, assured, and virile in his alertness. MODERATE MIXTURE, while neither outstandingly *Strong* like MUSCULAR, nor *Weak* and *Tense* like THIN, is *Assured* and *Virile* as is MUSCULAR.

As to speech, THIN showed inhibition in expression, although he was full of formulated ideas. MUSCULAR-FAT has no pronounced tendency which might suggest the mixed inclinations of our silent MUSCULARS and fluent FATS. MUSCULAR and MODERATE MIXTURE were *Formulated*—which makes sense in the light of field work experience. However, a *fluent* MUSCULAR was rare without the addition of noticeable FAT.

One last look at our five examples and then we must get to the laboratory. An item of particular interest was checked on the

MUSCULAR-FAT	Appearance and Expression: *Strong, Relaxed, Bland* Speech: *Medium*
MUSCULAR	Appearance and Expression: *Strong, Assured, Virile, Animated, Alert* Speech: *Fluent, Formulated*
MODERATE MIXTURE	Appearance and Expression: *Assured, Virile* Speech: *Formulated*
MUSCULAR-THIN	Appearance and Expression: *Medium* Speech: *Medium*
THIN	Appearance and Expression: *Weak, Tense, Animated, Alert* Speech: *Fluent, Formulated, Stammering*

Fig. 6 — APPEARANCE, EXPRESSION, AND SPEECH

Personality Inventories: Activities—with four degrees of incidence, marked by +++ ++ + 0 (see Figure 7).

Activities of the five types differ. THIN gets 0 in *Athletic* and *Mechanical,* but rates highest of all four types (+++) in *Cultural* and is the highest, with MUSCULAR-THIN, in *Ideational.* MUSCULAR-FAT is *more* athletic (++) than THIN, but *less* athletic than MUS-

CULAR. In the opposite direction, MUSCULAR-FAT is more *Ideational* than MUSCULAR, but two ranks below THIN.

MUSCULAR-THIN falls between THIN and MUSCULAR. He is *Mechanical* to an even higher degree than this MUSCULAR, although, in this instance, he is like THIN in being 0 in *Athletic*. (One other

MUSCULAR-FAT		THIN	
Athletic	++	Athletic	0
Mechanical	++	Mechanical	0
Executive	++	Executive	++
Ideational	+	Ideational	+++
Cultural	++	Cultural	+++

MODERATE MIXTURE	
Athletic	++
Mechanical	++
Executive	++
Ideational	++
Cultural	++

MUSCULAR		MUSCULAR-THIN	
Athletic	+++	Athletic	0
Mechanical	+	Mechanical	++
Executive	0	Executive	+++
Ideational	0	Ideational	+++
Cultural	++	Cultural	++

Fig. 7 — ACTIVITIES

MUSCULAR-THIN in the series was 0 in *Mechanical* and ranked two in *Athletic*.) It appears that a MUSCULAR-THIN, as we might expect, will approach THIN in some ways and approach MUSCULAR in others. He is some sort of combination of the two tendencies. Here, in *Executive, Ideational,* and *Cultural,* he is very close to THIN's ratings.

It will be noted that MODERATE MIXTURE is in second place (which would come near a middle range) in everything! He has no lacks—0's—and nothing over a two rating. Our good old MODERATE MIXTURE coming down the middle of the road again!

I have shown you a few Harvard University findings on our subjects before discussing the laboratory research itself so that you will not feel I am "making up" people myself. Also, on going over these medical records, we "disqualified" one subject who had a glandular abnormality. Otherwise, we considered the range of diseases and problems of interest, but not in the abnormal range.

The next thing we want to know is: how about the women? All right. Let's look at a few of them.

WOMEN IN SEDENTARY WORK

All were well enough and normal enough to hold down steady office jobs. Current doctor's examinations were not available, but medical histories were taken.

For our present purposes, let's look carefully at a female MUSCULAR-FAT, PLUMP-DELICATE, and MODERATE MIXTURE. This will give us male-female comparisons for two types of particular interest: MUSCULAR-FAT and MODERATE MIXTURE. We found no wholly THIN woman in our series, but the female PLUMP-DELICATE equates with the male THIN in some ways. Likewise FAT tendencies are recognizable in MUSCULAR-FATS. In the lab series, there were no extreme FATS.

Traits mentioned in the following chart (Figure 8) are a representative sampling of tendencies taken from items checked on a "temperament" form. This form was made up of items that were first noted by Sheldon as occurring most frequently with the three major body types. There was some overlapping of these traits. We will hold here to our familiar names: FAT, THIN, and MUSCULAR.

As you glance at MUSCULAR-FAT f. (female), you feel a correspondence with the man who was described in different words but with similar emphases. The THIN traits—which are here called DELICATE in the PLUMP-DELICATE—are very reminiscent of the THIN

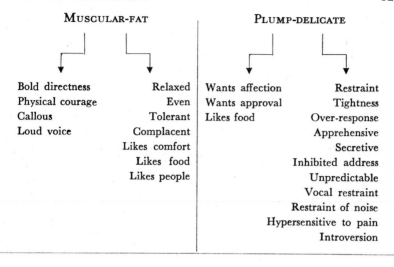

MUSCULAR-FAT		PLUMP-DELICATE	
Bold directness	Relaxed	Wants affection	Restraint
Physical courage	Even	Wants approval	Tightness
Callous	Tolerant	Likes food	Over-response
Loud voice	Complacent		Apprehensive
	Likes comfort		Secretive
	Likes food		Inhibited address
	Likes people		Unpredictable
			Vocal restraint
			Restraint of noise
			Hypersensitive to pain
			Introversion

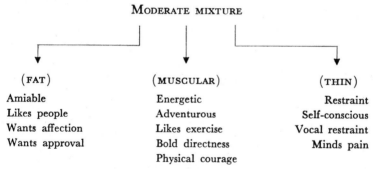

MODERATE MIXTURE		
(FAT)	(MUSCULAR)	(THIN)
Amiable	Energetic	Restraint
Likes people	Adventurous	Self-conscious
Wants affection	Likes exercise	Vocal restraint
Wants approval	Bold directness	Minds pain
	Physical courage	

Fig. 8 — TENDENCIES OF TEMPERAMENT

college man. MODERATE MIXTURE again goes down the middle of the road with tendencies—though not extreme—which can be found in all three major directions: FAT, MUSCULAR, and THIN.

Before going to the tests themselves, we might like to glance at a brief summary of the assortment of so-called traits of "temperament" from which the items on Figure 8 came. The three major tendencies Sheldon noticed have been grouped under four headings for each type. We will use the body type terms: FAT, THIN, and MUSCULAR.

Fat

Fat tendencies that appeared to "go with" body build may be summarized briefly under headings of Physical, Social, and Emotional —plus a Statement as to Appearance of Maturity:

Physical: Fats were apt to be relaxed in posture and movement, loved physical comfort, tended to have slow reactions. They loved eating and took pleasure in digestion.

Social: They liked eating with other people and enjoyed polite ceremony of various kinds. They liked people in general and had indiscriminate amiability with a greed for affection and approval. They were definitely oriented to *people* and needed people when they were troubled. Under the influence of alcohol, fats relaxed in line with their physical tendencies and enjoyed sociability in line with their social tendencies.

Emotional: An evenness of emotional flow accompanied the slowness of reaction mentioned above. Fats had smooth, easy communication of feeling; they tended to be "benign" extroverts. Their basic feelings made for attitudes of tolerance and complacency. They enjoyed deep, untroubled sleep when night came.

Statement as to Appearance of Maturity: Fats tended to have placid, "unwritten" faces with the general appearance of lack of harsh life experience—a so-called "untempered" look to their whole person. They often were oriented toward childhood and family relationships.

Thin

Thin tendencies were almost polar opposites to fat trends:

Physical: Thins showed restraint in posture and movement, suffered from tightness, and tended to have overly fast reactions. They were apt to have mental overintensity, hyperattention in general, with underlying apprehension. A self-conscious motility of eyes and face was often noticeable.

Social: It is not surprising with these reactions that thins did not share fats' love of people but had a love of privacy. When troubled, they wanted solitude—to be left alone. THINS often had a fear of social occasions—"sociophobia." With their vocal restraint and general restraint of noise went a tendency to inhibited social address. They resisted alcohol and other depressant drugs, so "easy cheer and relaxation with friends" was not a "natural" for them.

Emotional: Emotional restraint and secretiveness of feeling found privacy more congenial than sociability. There was even a prevalence of fear of wide-open spaces (agoraphobia). There tended to be resistance to regularity of routine and a general unpredictability of attitude. THINS were introverts rather than happy (FAT) extroverts; instead of being smooth outgoing social communicators in a "horizontal" direction toward their fellows, they tended to have their feelings directed in a "vertical" plane. They were introspective rather than outgoing. When you add to these reactions a hyper-sensitivity to various kinds of pain, it becomes apparent why these people did not enjoy the deep, untroubled slumber of FATS and were a prey to chronic fatigue when wrongly situated in life.

Statement as to Appearance of Maturity: THINS had a perennially youthful intentness of manner and appearance. However, in their thoughts, they were oriented toward the later periods of life.

MUSCULAR

MUSCULARS reflected their strength in many ways:

Physical: They had assertiveness of posture and movement, the energetic characteristic, a need and enjoyment of exercise, and a love of physical adventure. They loved risk and chance. They had physical courage for combat.

Social: Their unrestrained voice and psychological callousness gave them a bold directness of manner which implemented their competitive aggressiveness in relation to other people. They were generally noisy and showed assertiveness and aggression when under the influence of alcohol. When troubled, they neither needed people—like FATS—nor avoided people—like THINS—but had a need of action.

Emotional: With their psychological callousness noted above went a love of dominating and a lust for power. They showed frequent ruthlessness and freedom from squeamishness and a Spartan indifference to pain. It is clear they were outgoing and extrovert but in a very MUSCULAR way as compared to the "benign" extroversion of FATS. The socially "horizontal" behavior of MUSCULARS has to be specially labelled: the Extroversion of MUSCULARS. With their prevalent need for action, they tended to feel uncomfortable in small, closed spaces (claustrophobia).

Statement as to Appearance of Maturity: MUSCULARS had an "overmaturity" of appearance but were definitely oriented to the goals and activities of youth. Their "mature" look made boys look older than they were as contrasted with the "juvenile" look of adult THINS.

There is much I should like to say about each of the twenty-five subjects whom I grew to know so well. Minor differences of emphasis and combinations of tendencies were noticeable as we looked at findings "under the microscope." Careful study of the few people who deviated in behavior from the general trends of their type was of particular interest.

At present, however, we are not concerned with minor differences or deviants; we want to know: how did the different types behave on the tests. Let's look at typical examples.

17. What Does a Test TEST?
or
DIFFERENT People Take Tests

LET'S LOOK AT TEST RESULTS for MUSCULAR-FAT m. (male) and MUSCULAR-FAT f. (female); for MUSCULAR m. and MUSCULAR-THIN m.; for THIN m. and PLUMP-DELICATE f.; and for MODERATE MIXTURE m. and f.

CAN YOU KEEP YOUR EYE ON THE TARGET?

Our first tests used a "contraption" called a targetometer or pursuitmeter. The subject had to make paired light beams follow a randomly moving target. The task was exacting and boring over a long period of time. The steering mechanism resembled the stick of a plane. Like stitching, it required eye, foot, and hand co-ordination. The subject "scored" for the length of time he could keep the beams on the target. The test lasted from one to four hours.

Before we began the tests reported here, the targetometer was used to show performance as influenced by drugs. Some people had the drug and others a "placebo" (sugar pill) which they thought was the drug. There were not striking differences in our subjects as to which were taking pills and which were not. However, subjects differed in their performance.

At that time we began the preliminary trial tests referred to above (p. 113). The four college men who made these early runs were two pronounced MUSCULARS and two typical MUSCULAR-THINS. The MUSCULAR-THINS were high in THIN traits with moderate MUSCULAR support. They were definitely MUSCULAR-*THINS,* not THIN-*MUSCULARS.* The first thing that caught our attention was the difference in reaction between the two kinds of subjects.

When a MUSCULAR and a MUSCULAR-THIN ran simultaneously and talked to each other, the MUSCULAR man could keep his paired light right on the target most of the time. MUSCULAR-THIN, on the other hand, scored poorly, and would even turn and look at the other fellow when the conversation interested him. It relieved his boredom, but certainly did not help his score. He was definitely the more distractible of the two. Later tests on these subjects in the organized series bore out these tendencies.

For proper interpretation of differences, there were many things I needed to know. I wanted to become better acquainted with our subjects. I got health and social histories, physical and emotional data. I summarized my impressions of different subjects.

Of the first MUSCULAR I wrote:

Quiet. Not excitable. He says, "I am never startled." Slow, neutral, and negatively toned reactions usually. However, he likes the mechanical aspects of the test. He likes machines. Likes the targetometer. He likes good instruments: a long slide rule, pin point calipers.

Not introspective. He claims not to "think" unless there is a reason to. Thinks of the mind as something you don't overwork uselessly. Only think when a problem of your job to tackle. He has had many heavy jobs and has been a truck driver. When driving, would go two or three hours "without thinking anything," he said.

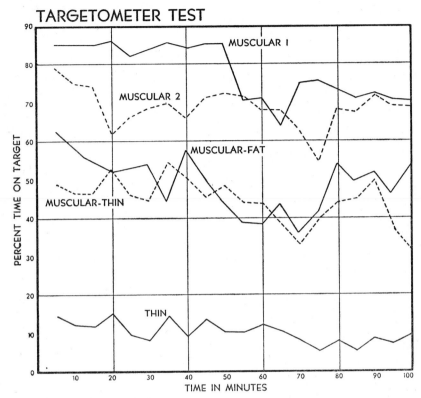

Fig. 9 — DIFFERENCES IN SCORING ABILITY ON THE
TARGETOMETER TEST

You will not be surprised to learn that this MUSCULAR was a quick learner and a consistently high scorer on the targetometer (see Figure 9). Noise and talking did not affect his score. Like others, he scored better with music and made a slight spurt.

The second MUSCULAR made runs which were very similar to the first MUSCULAR. He was a high, relatively even performer. Of his personality impression I wrote:

Stable. Doesn't get excitably upset. Even. Good-natured, strong, unemotional. He is not overreactive nor sluggish. A certain lack of sharpness of intellect is definitely present. He is very different from the THIN cerebral variety of individual. . . .

The Harvard Hygiene Department had rated him +++ on *Athletic* and *Mechanical* Activities, but 0 on *Executive* and *Ideational*. Of his personality, they checked: *Energy, Stable, Even*, but also *Bland* and *Warm*. I had noted the lack of "unpleasant" aggression.

He seemed like a "happy" MUSCULAR. The Hygiene Department gave him every positive character and social trait: *Dependable, Steady, Contented, Adaptable, Controlled, Poised, Spontaneous, Initiative*, plus *Leader, Friendly, Cooperative*, and *Natural*.

As to favorite recreations, he listed for me: *FOOTBALL*
fishing
baseball
handball
hiking
swimming

("pretty complete," he said.)

MUSCULAR-THIN's list of recreations contrasted with MUSCULAR's. MUSCULAR-*THIN* told me, *"Reading is what I do most!"* When he had pneumonia, he ruined his eyes by reading a thousand pages a day. While he did weight lifting for a year and a half—when he was 15—he said he'd done other sports "a little" but didn't like them especially. His brother swung a bat when they were playing baseball and hit MUSCULAR-THIN's teeth. MUSCULAR-THIN was also hurt playing football, and broke his nose when he fell downstairs.

I wrote of MUSCULAR-THIN:

Alert, eager, intellectual. Apprehensive and tense in new situation (as when learning to score on targetometer). Highly reactive to stimuli. Fatigable. Cannot "do anything" at night after a four-hour run on the targetometer. Has to go to bed.

Puts "reading" ahead of all other "recreation"! [Note: reading not mentioned by either MUSCULAR as recreation.]

Intense about college work. Stays up all night before exam.

Takes benzedrine. High-keyed. Ambitious. Hopes to get some "A's." Never "relaxed." Nervous, reactive.

Musical. Sensitive to rhythm. Beats time with hand to popular tune.

His performance on the targetometer fell below the two MUS-CULARS (Figure 9). He was a slow learner and was distracted by talking, as already noted above. Noise bothered MUSCULAR-THIN and music picked him up noticeably. However, even under optimum conditions of pleasing music, his scoring never approached the consistently high scoring of the MUSCULARS.

On the Subjective Analysis sheet used to check personal feelings before and after the test, MUSCULAR-THIN tended to check higher degrees of strain than MUSCULARS. MUSCULAR number one was often in the midrange of indifference. MUSCULAR number two often went into the test feeling peppy and came out in nearly as happy a state. MUSCULAR-THIN often went into the test in an indifferent mood and came out a little the worse for wear. Sometimes, however, he could maintain a stoic "indifference."

After getting this well acquainted with the two MUSCULARS and one MUSCULAR-THIN in the test situation, we are curious to see a full-fledged THIN reacting to music, noise, and the targetometer. And how about MUSCULAR-FAT?

While MUSCULAR-THIN compared unfavorably with MUSCULAR as to high, even scoring, it is interesting to find that MUSCULAR-THIN and MUSCULAR-FAT were fairly similar in degree of proficiency while *a real* (extreme) THIN was about as low a scorer as a person could be and still score at all! (Look at the bottom of Figure 9.) A glance at MUSCULAR-FAT's average scores under a good many test situations, as compared with THIN's performance, made THIN's results look pitiful! He wasn't even "in the running!"

Therefore, we might infer from this data that MUSCULARS are "supermen" at this type of test, MUSCULAR-THINS and MUSCULAR-FATS are good, while THINS are "no good." We may recall THIN got "0" in *Mechanical* Activities.

In comparing my comments about the two MUSCULARS and

MUSCULAR-THIN with observations on THIN, we find he offered an extreme picture of THIN alertness and excitability. I said:

Definitely insecure, escapist behavior though good mental equipment and many admirable qualities. Can work well when holds to routine. Tends to waste time with friends and seek security in drink, unconventional behavior, etc. High sigher and trouble with swallowing during periods of life crisis. This is a talented person but frail and insecure. Parents' divorce bad for this boy. Rejection of family support. Needs "stabilization."

The comments of the Hygiene Department were as follows:

Examiner's Impression: Impresses me as highly sensitive, introspective, and delicate, but also intelligent. Parents divorced, 4F in draft as Psych. Slight stammer to speech and has gagging attacks.

The army was probably wise in considering THIN a psychological 4F for army duty. However, as he was not psychologically unfit for college work, and, in fact, was a very satisfactory student, he was not considered unsuitable for this research. That he was an extreme and highly reactive THIN made his reactions particularly significant as a polar extreme. That he sometimes manifested psychosomatic symptoms in reaction to stress fitted into the scope of this particular study of nervous strain.

As to his health history, I had noted an attack of pneumonia at the time of his parents' separation. Otherwise, only children's diseases were listed on his Hygiene account, and the common tonsillectomy and appendectomy plus notation of "slight nervousness from 6-18 years." At the time of our tests, he was 19. THIN was not a "sick" boy—he never took medicine—but he was a nervous boy. Natural endowment and life experience had not given him "all aces."

With MUSCULAR-FAT, it was different. While he had had children's diseases and his tonsils out, and had even broken a leg, he lived under no strain. When I asked him about his home situation, he replied casually—as though it were the common lot of all—"Oh, I have a lot of fun at home."

Among other comments about him, I noted:

Jovial, easygoing, pleasant. Carefree. Likes family life. Not mind about going into army. Open. . . .

The Hygiene Department had confidence in him.

Examiner's Impression: Pleasant, cooperative, intelligent, ambitious young man here on part-scholarship, part-loan, and part-earnings (working while in school). Has the ambition to attain his goal.

MUSCULAR-FAT held some "aces."

WHAT MUSIC "AGREES" WITH YOU?

I think we are well enough acquainted with these subjects and their customary (so-called *"Control"*) performance on the targetometer to look at some of the other runs. A brief résumé of the most striking results of targetometer tests with music and noise (half an hour in the last half of the run) are tabulated for us in Table 15.

The main points to bear in mind are:

The *Marches, Rhumbas,* and *Polkas* used on one test were all fast, lively, loud orchestral numbers.

By contrast, the *Bing Crosby* program was made up entirely of soft, "croony-swoony" sentimental songs.

The *Unfamiliar Music* was all lively but foreign (from Armenia and neighboring regions) and unfamiliar to all but one of the subjects. Pieces were both instrumental and vocal. They were played and sung in native renditions.

While early tests had used bells (of doorbell type) for intermittent noise, the series shown in this chart used *Noise* recordings of various rasping sounds.

Naturally we want to know how THIN and MUSCULAR-FAT fared on these tests. The pronounced MUSCULARS, whose high scores you saw in Figure 9, had left before this series was initiated. We shall have to content ourselves with reactions of some rather mixed MUSCULARS whom we shall call MODERATE MIXTURE—MUSCULARS. They

TABLE 15

REACTIONS OF DIFFERENT TYPES TO
MUSIC AND NOISE DURING THE TARGETOMETER TEST

	PER CENT TIME ON TARGET							
	THIN		TWO MODERATE MIXTURE—MUSCULARS				MUSCULAR-FAT	
STIMULUS	First 30 minutes	Stimulus second 30 minutes	First 30 minutes	Stimulus second 30 minutes	First 30 minutes	Stimulus second 30 minutes	First 30 minutes	Stimulus second 30 minutes
Marches, Rhumbas, and Polkas	15	6	41——▶47		39——▶45		60	47
Bing Crosby	14	7.5	47.5	33	36	35	57	45
Unfamiliar	26	24	43——▶62		33	25	63	45
Noise	14	12	46	44	40	18	53	28

▶ Notes improved scoring
═══ Notes lowered scoring

had a definite emphasis on MUSCULAR, but were also noticeably developed in the other two trends. While they were not poor performers, they did not approach the scoring ability of the full-fledged MUSCULARS.

Four points "hit" us in Table 15:

1. MODERATE MIXTURE—MUSCULARS improved with marches while THIN's biggest drop was on a march.

2. No one improved his scoring during the "croony-swoony" Bing Crosby pieces.

3. Unfamiliar (foreign) music agreed *only* with the subject to whom the music was familiar. He markedly improved his score.

4. Noise caused a drastic drop in the scoring ability of MUSCULAR-FAT and one of the MODERATE MIXTURE—MUSCULARS.

As to the varying effects of noise, the fact that MODERATE MIXTURE—MUSCULARS score less well than pronounced MUSCULARS and appear to mind noise more probably should not surprise us. MUSCULAR-FAT said he didn't "like" the noise but didn't "mind" it. However, his test results show that while his disposition was not complaining, his performance was.

THIN sighed five or six times with noise and unfamiliar music as compared with from none to three on all other runs. The fact that he sighed about twice as often on the noise and unfamiliar music tests may signify greater nervous strain, even though he was kept alert by the irritant and his score didn't drop much. (The deep sighs noted on these tests were audible to the observer. Later breathing tests measured sighs in greater detail.)

ARE YOU A HIGH SIGHER?

I have just read over my preliminary scientific analysis of our lab experiments on breathing. We tested people on pleasant and unpleasant thoughts, in situations of being startled, relaxed, or praised. We measured many things: breathing volume, oxygen consumed, variability of breathing pattern, sighs. Authorities—like Finesinger of the Massachusetts General Hospital in Boston and J. L. Caughey, Jr., then at the Presbyterian Hospital in New York—were quoted. Our series was shown to be similar in varieties to larger studies.

In my quest for new knowledge, I was most impressed by Dr. Finesinger's comment to me that "if we knew *why* people sighed, we'd know the source of anxiety." I was also interested to know *who* sighed about *what*. Hooton's[8] summary in *Young Man, You Are Normal* had pointed out that of the *less well-integrated* Harvard college men studied by the Grant Study, nearly half (45 per cent) were excessive sighers (defined as "more than three sighs in two minutes during a basal [resting] metabolism"). As Caughey summed up the situation, "From a clinical point of view, the appearance of many sighs on a spirogram indicates some kind of emotional or neuro-muscular tension during the recording."

Table 16 presents some sigh data from our tests and gives us a quick impression of "how the wind was blowing" with some of the subjects we know best. MUSCULAR-FAT m. and MUSCULAR-FAT f. both sighed only four times on a total of eight tests! The ninth test—praise—was missed by some subjects, so it is not included on these

[8]Earnest A. Hooton (New York: G. P. Putnam's Sons, 1945).

totals. Plump-delicate sighed fourteen times and thin m. topped the score sheet with eighty-one sighs. On his basal metabolism test,

TABLE 16
Sigh Data

Fat-Mus-cular "Sport" m.		Muscular-Fat		Mus-cular m.	Mus-cular-Thin m.	Thin m.	Plump-Delicate f.	Moderate Mixture	
		m.	f.					m.	f.
4	Learning	1	0			4	1	0	0
2	Before	0	0			1	0	0	0
4900	Vital capacity	4450	2330			1370	2230	4520	1600
0	After vital capacity	1	0			1	1	1	0
4	Before	0	0			4	0	0	0
0	4 min. writing (30 sec. intervals)	0	0			2	0	0	0
8	4 min. between writing (30 sec. intervals)	0	0	Non-sigher	Sighed occasionally	2	0	0	0
4	After	0	0			4	0	0	1
1	Before	0	0			5	0	0	0
1	4 min. pleasant	0	0			2	0	0	0
2	4 min. unpleasant	0	0			1	1	1	0
1	After	0	1			3	0	0	1
3	Before Dot Test	0	0			5	0	0	0
1	4 min. #1 Dot Test	0	0			0	0	1	0
4	4 min. betw. #1 Dot Test	0	2			9	2	0	0
8	After	0	0			5	0	0	1
5	Before	0	0			4	0	2	0
2	Pleasant #2	0	0			3	2	0	0
1	Unpleasant #2	0	0			3	2	0	1
6	After	0	1			5	1	0	1
3	Before	0	0			4	0	0	0
2	4 min. Dot startle	1	0			0	2	0	0
5	4 min. betw. Dot startle	1	0			7	1	1	1
7	After	0	0			3	0	0	0
2	4 min. relaxation	0	0			2	0	0	0
2	4 min. after relaxation	0	0			2	1	0	0
0	4 min. praise		0				0	0	0
0	4 min. after		0				1*	0	0
78	Total Sighs†	4	4			81	14	6	6

*Omitted from totals as this test not taken by all subjects.
†"Vital capacity," in c.c., not a part of Sigh totals.

he sighed *less* than three sighs in two minutes—about one sigh in two minutes.

Two THIN women, who were less extreme than the male THIN we have described, had a total of from seventeen to nineteen sighs. In other words, they were a little over PLUMP-DELICATE and the next-highest sighers to the extreme THIN, but their totals were not nearly so high as his. We shall mention them again later.

MODERATE MIXTURES m. and f. were very like the MUSCULAR-FATS (four sighs). Both MODERATE MIXTURES sighed six times in all.

The two MUSCULARS, whom we have seen top the targetometer performance, showed only one sigh between them. They were run on a different group of tests, however, so data, while of interest, are not identical. Nevertheless, it is very evident from their control tests that neither was a habitual, or even frequent sigher, as is the case with THIN (the two less-extreme THINS also) and PLUMP-DELICATE.

Pleasant and Unpleasant Thoughts

Now I know you want to know *who* sighed about *what*. We "pinned the thoughts down" by having the subject write what he was thinking. I noted any sighing on the spirogram and the word he was writing at the time. Later I made an arrow over the word on his "thought" sheet for each minute of the test.

Finesinger had initiated tests on pleasant and unpleasant reverie. I was trying to get just a little more specific. It might help locate "sore spots" in the individual's adjustment. Also, I had them *write* the thoughts so that we could study and analyze them later in comparison with other subjects. A writing control run ruled out the effect of using a pencil. We had *two* pleasant-unpleasant tests for each subject to be sure the results were not "freaky."

First we'll summarize totals, then look at particular "thoughts." You will see (Table 17) that neither MUSCULAR-FAT (m. or f.) sighed on any Pleasant or Unpleasant period (each period lasted four minutes). MODERATE MIXTURES m. and f. both sighed once on one of the Unpleasant periods. In sharp contrast to MUSCULAR-FATS

TABLE 17

Sighs During Pleasant and Unpleasant Thoughts

		Muscular-fat		Thin	Plump-delicate	Moderate-mixture	
		m.	f.	m.	f.	m.	f.
I							
	Pleasant	0	0	2	0	0	0
	Unpleasant	0	0	1	1	1	0
II							
	Pleasant	0	0	3	2	0	0
	Unpleasant	0	0	3	2	0	1
Totals		0	0			1	1

and MODERATE MIXTURES, PLUMP-DELICATE and THIN sighed on all but one of the periods—PLUMP-DELICATE totalling five sighs and THIN hitting the high of nine sighs.

To get a glimpse into a few thoughts of our different types, I'll show you what different ones wrote on one of their Pleasant-Unpleasant tests. Where subjects sighed, I'll put "sigh" in brackets. First, let's get the feel of the two MUSCULAR-FATS so that we may compare them with later samples. While the situation was, of course, artificial, it was under the same conditions for the whole group. Like the "spontaneous comments" in the factory, it was of interest to see what people would "choose" to say.[9]

MUSCULAR-FAT m.

MUSCULAR-FAT wrote:

(pleasant thoughts)

The day was like any other December day—the sky was cloudy and there was a bite to the air. But inside our home it was not just another day, it was December 25. Christmas. My sister and I,—I, 11, and she 8,—got up a[t] six and went into the living room. There under the tree were all sorts of things.

[9]Pleasant and unpleasant thoughts, as test data, are unedited. Names fictitious.

My sister had a beautiful doll and dishes and such. I just sat there. I had expected a bicycle, but there was not one here. Suddenly, I heard a honk honk behind me. My father was wheeling in a brand new bicycle, honking the horn. It was all for me! I was very proud that day.

(unpleasant thoughts)

I don't know why but I was feeling mean that day. I came home, feeling cross and angry. I had no reason to be though, the spring was just beginning, and buds could be seen on some of the trees. It wouldn't be long until I could go and play all day long; but here I was feeling cross, angry and hot. My father knew I was sick and told me to go to bed. I did it reluctantly, and was mad when he called the doctor. Then the doctor said it. I had the measles. Right in the most beautiful part of the year. I spent three weeks in bed, in a darkened room, with nothing to do. Was I burned up!

COMMENTS: On MUSCULAR-FAT's other run, he gave an account of his experience at a boys' camp in the West. The first section described the beauties of nature. The "unpleasant" run told about how rain spoiled plans for a big gala day at camp. They got up and dressed in the rain and cold, only to get to the mess hall and be told:

"So Sorry [deep breath, but not quite a sigh], boys; but we close at eight o'clock. Better get [another breath somewhat deeper than usual] up earlier tomorrow."

I think you will notice MUSCULAR-FAT's reflection of a happy home life, love of the outdoors, and usually good disposition (his father "*knew* he was sick" and MUSCULAR-FAT was amazed to find himself in a cross mood). He did reflect a little change in his breathing pattern with the thoughts of "no breakfast" and "getting up early"! These stresses involve loss of food and sleep. These comments may reflect FAT leanings.

MUSCULAR-FAT f.

MUSCULAR-FAT f. wrote:

(pleasant thoughts)

Ted home again for eight or ten days. What will we do tonight? How about Pops?

Betty is all set now. Everything has been taken care of. She's pleased, I'm pleased, we're all pleased!

Our new living room set looks lovely. Very comfortable and good-looking. Sturdy, too!

Philip has been found at last. He isn't dead, after all. The marked grave was a mistake.

(unpleasant thoughts)

The veterinary certainly made a wreck of the dog. His fur is all matted and yellow. Should we have him clipped now, poor thing? He would have to be completely shaved to make everything fine again. I surely wish something could be done for Bob. He's such a fine fellow, it's a shame he has to be mentally deficient for the rest of his life.

What hard luck Nellie has had this year. First she lost her husband, then her health, then her home. Now her mother is on the way out after a long illness. Some people don't realize how lucky they [are].

COMMENTS: After this test, MUSCULAR-FAT told me it was "very hard to think of unpleasant things." Her sympathy and love of people is very noticeable throughout all her comments. This has been noted as a feature of FAT tendencies.

In her other test, she discussed her delight at receiving a box of candy and cashew nuts. She wanted to give a relative some. She wrote:

Wonderful candy! Every piece is different. And the cashews were a real treat. It's a long time since I've had any. It sort of whets the appetite! I must look around for some more. Maybe I could find some for the boys.

Pop Punch and cashews—what a combination!

Her thoughts of food have a FAT feeling, as does her comment on the first test about the *comfort* of the new furniture. She also mentions that it is *sturdy*. Love of comfort has been pointed out for FATS and the sturdiness might be a reflection of MUSCULAR leanings.

THIN m.

Now let's listen to THIN's thoughts:

(pleasant thoughts)

Spring in New York—Art Galleries on a sunny, very quiet afternoon—bicycle riding [sigh] in early Fall—canoeing during an
Midnight on lake—listening to medieval plain chants
Wm. Blake—Shakespeare's Sonnets—
[sigh] The train trips home from anywhere—the feeling of accomplishment obtained after difficult assignment has been completed—

(unpleasant thoughts)

Two of my room-mates—radio late at night blaring—
Poor food—loud, coarse manners—
deceitfulness both in [sigh] people and in art—over-humility—
flattery and obsequiousness—

That THIN sighs when he thinks of *bicycle riding* may not be too great a surprise. He is not athletic. MUSCULAR-FAT's happiness over his new bicycle caused him no emotional conflict. Also, the fact that THIN sighs before he writes "The train trips home from anywhere" is understandable when we realize he really has no "home" but an apartment of his own in a big city. He also sighed before he wrote "the reunion with family" as his first "pleasant" thought on the other run. He sighed while writing "moving apart" on the other unpleasant run. Although this was in connection with a boy he liked, yet the experience had a familiar "ring" in his life.

His sigh about *deceitfulness in people* is certainly a far cry from

MUSCULAR-FAT reactions. Our feminine MUSCULAR-FAT would never say such a thing!

On his other test, THIN sighed once on "grayness" and once on "winter." He complained of the "lack of warmth and barrier of coldness" in New England. These were "unpleasant" thoughts to him. They somehow echoed the bleakness of his life and the fact that THIN had little to shield him from the cold of life relationships or the actual cold. Perhaps we should say he was "thin-skinned." He probably did "mind" the cold as many THIN people do. Cold also symbolizes rejection and lack of warmth in social relationships. While, as THIN explained to me, he had "his own group of intellectuals," he hated many people. Dislike was a common reaction with him. He had keen social awareness and sensitivity which made him acutely uncomfortable and unhappy in many situations.

He also minded *noise*. When I queried him about his thought about *poor food,* he said he was referring to the college dining room. There's such a "racket" in there too, he added. Now we see why it made him happy to think of "a *sunny, very quiet* afternoon."

PLUMP-DELICATE f.

What does PLUMP-DELICATE have to say:

(pleasant thoughts)

I still get a bit of a thrill when I think of the lovely wallet I received from my brother yesterday morning—it was such a nice thought, particular
In getting together with the cousin I haven't seen in a long while, I found such fun. Uncle gave us a talk on our ancestry and background and what happened during his young manhood. I marvelled that at 76, he still could be a majestic figure and could reminisce with such clarity for details and date. I'm glad I have a bit of his blood in me and wish I

(unpleasant thoughts)

Is a shock unpleasant—I guess it is and yet, in a way, I should have expected it. I don't like to see co-workers whom I have enjoyed working with leave. Makes the thought of a new worker most disagreeable.

I don't know what to say when I get back because I will be asked all sorts of questions and none of which I can answer.

I guess I'm not a good actress because my expression will give me away

[sigh] I just can see now days ahead of pressure, dutiful thinking and conscientious work to get a week's pay without the little snatches of gaiety and fun and frankness.

COMMENTS: PLUMP-DELICATE sighed before "I just can see now days of pressure ahead." Knowing her as well as I did, I could catch overtones to the remarks which would not be obvious to a person unacquainted with the subject. When she began her unpleasant thoughts with "Is a shock unpleasant—I guess it is and yet, in a way, I should have expected it," it "rang a bell" with me for at almost every test session she came to me with some great "crisis" which had just come upon her. Something *terrible* had *just* happened to her. As few subjects presented these perpetual tragedies, this comment was a characteristic one. Her seeing only "days of pressure" ahead was not surprising.

She shows a PLUMP liking for people with an overlay of THIN lack of "universal" liking of people. The assumption that the new worker would be *disagreeable* was a part of this latent distrust—although a natural feeling to some extent.

MODERATE MIXTURE f.

As a means of evaluating PLUMP-DELICATE's reactions, it is of interest to compare them with a feminine MODERATE MIXTURE. This woman was roughly the same age and had a secretarial job. While I saw her a great deal and discussed problem areas of her life, she never arrived with "crises" as PLUMP-DELICATE did. The fact that her husband was on active war duty at the time would have been sufficient reason.

When I explained the Pleasant-Unpleasant test to her, she said that she didn't have happy or unhappy events in her life. She was "neutral." How like a MODERATE MIXTURE. She accepted the feelings of general anxiety and relative boredom which she had at times as a "part of the game" and took them in stride.

She wrote:

(pleasant thoughts)

My new job
Flowers that a neighbor brings
Watching my garden
Sun bathing
Walking in springtime
Visits with
A week end with old friends in the country

(unpleasant thoughts)

A visit from a couple who are boring—formal and not natural—whom you suspect of using you—
Disappointment about vacation plans and my husband's furlough being deferred.
Too much housework

MODERATE MIXTURE f.'s only sigh on the two runs was at the beginning of the second *Unpleasant* thoughts before the comment: Normandy—casualties—.

Certainly, with her husband on active duty, this was a "normal" sigh.

MODERATE MIXTURE m.

MODERATE MIXTURE, masculine college version, wrote:

(pleasant thoughts)

During September I was out at Trainersville to debate. On my way back I stopped at Wight College, where I looked up a girl whom I had heard about from my father and from a friend of mine. This friend gave me two names to look up, but I stopped after meeting the first girl. I met her at about twelve o'clock, and she showed me

all around the Wight campus, which is the most beautiful college
campus I've ever seen. I left at about five o'clock that night. I had
had a wonderful week end, and meeting her really topped it off.
Who knows,
[and he had put on the back of the sheet:] Who knows—maybe
I'm in love?

(unpleasant thoughts)

Early last term I began a course known as History I, supposed to
be the toughest but best course in Harvard. I determined to work
very hard, and I did. Averaging fifteen to sixteen hours a week.
I put more into that course than I had ever done before in any
course. I considered myself well prepared for every test. And yet
I could never get a good mark. I was consistently a low B or B-,
or occasionally [sigh] a high C. One mark, my collateral report,
pulled me up to a low B average.

Then I crammed terrifically for the final. But two dates fouled
me up. I got a 74.5 on the final. I worked up with a 75.18 average
(previously miscomputed)

COMMENTS: I don't know whether you happen to have known
many American college boys, but, for my money, this one sounds
like about as normal and satisfactory a guy as any parent could
hope to send off to college. He seems to have picked up the most
desirable feature of all three trends: intellectual enough (THIN),
some aggression and self-assertion (MUSCULAR) mostly directed
towards his college work or debating, social (FAT) in a constructive
way. He works, he plays, he thinks.

In sharp contrast to both him and the adjusted MUSCULAR-FAT
college boy above was a maladjusted MUSCULAR-FAT who was almost
as high a sigher as THIN. I put in these comments at this time so
that we will all realize where those people come from about whom
people always say, "Oh, but I've known a strong, heavy athlete
who wasn't anything like your description of MUSCULAR-FATS," or
"I know a 'mean' FAT," or "I know a calm, sociable THIN." I
agree. I've known them too. You can find them, but they are

"sports" and in the minority. That is, they are the "exceptions that prove the rule."

Figures 10 and 11 on pages 146 and 147 show the correspondence between the office and factory appraisals for body build and those for behavior, temperament, personality—or whatever you want to call it. You will see that trends are roughly similar but not identical. A person very used to evaluating people is surprised when he gets these atypical manifestations. A psychologist begins hunting in the case history to see how the person "got that way."

This can happen to a FAT and make him a morose misanthrope (people-hater!), or can change an anxious THIN to a secure, sociable guy, or upset a MODERATE MIXTURE. Exactly what happens to each one is doubtless different. Here we will discuss what happened to a MUSCULAR-FAT "sport." His "changing" experience seems to be largely in relation to his MUSCULAR propensities with effect on his sociable FAT leanings. Let's take a look at the situation.

M U S C U L A R - F A T m. (sport)

(As the emphasis was more on MUSCULAR, technically we had better call this fellow a FAT-*MUSCULAR*). FAT-*MUSCULAR* had severe adjustment problems. He had high MUSCULAR emphasis but had never had a chance to exercise as a growing boy. His family lived in a big city apartment at the time. Later, when he got where he could do things outside, he said he was embarrassed to do everything so poorly. In college he went in for rowing and this was helping some. However, from his thoughts on one of his Pleasant-Unpleasant tests, you will see he had problems—was under "some kind of emotional tension," as Caughey would say.

His "pleasant" thoughts were:

(pleasant thoughts)

In a month I shall see my family again. I haven't seen them for some time—my father I saw six months ago, but only for twenty-four hours, in a New York hotel [sigh]. The rest of my family I saw last in August, a year ago.

We are going to rent a house with a piano out in the country (in the West). We shall be able to sing and play around it. By playing I mean playing chamber music. We shall be able to play piano trios only, since—

His "unpleasant" thoughts were:

(unpleasant thoughts)

This term I am on pro, because of an E made last term and because of "unsatisfactory attendance." This phrase (of the making of the Dean's office) means that for about a month during the term I didn't attend classes [sigh] at all. I just sat in my room and simmered internally, a simmer caused of shame, rage at myself, and fear. or I could go out and row, thus taking my mind off my thoughts. Or I would do serious, but non-course reading, such as Chaucer, thus feeling that I was doing something worthwhile. I liked Chaucer so much that I am now taking Farrell's English [000], a course on Middle English.

I didn't really expect—

COMMENTS: I think we have become well enough acquainted with various combinations of MUSCULAR and FAT traits in the factory and laboratory so that we recognize the fact that the college boy just described is not "typical" of his body build. He needs more frequent outlet for his athletic potentialities. He needs to become skillful enough at a sport or dancing so that it will not make him "shy"— which, by now, you will realize is not "usual" social behavior for a person with FAT in his make-up. This FAT-MUSCULAR might be quiet like the strong, silent MUSCULARS; but we wouldn't expect him to shut himself up in a room with a book!

Now what kind of person might do that? I know your guess is as good as mine: people with THIN emphasis. The point about our THIN example is that he is an *extreme*, not a deviant in his behavior. The two feminine THINS are very like him, except they just don't go as far in the direction as he does. For instance, one of the THIN women is afraid to answer the door when someone rings the bell.

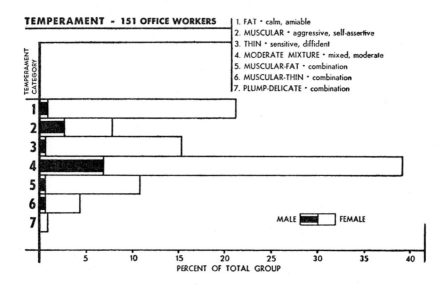

TEMPERAMENT - 151 OFFICE WORKERS

1. FAT • calm, amiable
2. MUSCULAR • aggressive, self-assertive
3. THIN • sensitive, diffident
4. MODERATE MIXTURE • mixed, moderate
5. MUSCULAR-FAT • combination
6. MUSCULAR-THIN • combination
7. PLUMP-DELICATE • combination

TEMPERAMENT CATEGORY

MALE   FEMALE

PERCENT OF TOTAL GROUP

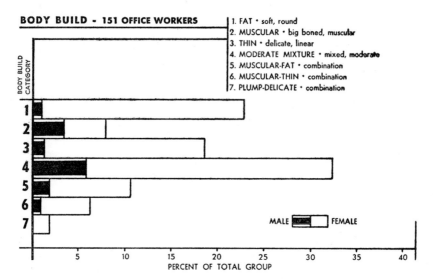

BODY BUILD - 151 OFFICE WORKERS

1. FAT • soft, round
2. MUSCULAR • big boned, muscular
3. THIN • delicate, linear
4. MODERATE MIXTURE • mixed, moderate
5. MUSCULAR-FAT • combination
6. MUSCULAR-THIN • combination
7. PLUMP-DELICATE • combination

BODY BUILD CATEGORY

MALE   FEMALE

PERCENT OF TOTAL GROUP

Fig. 10 — COMPARATIVE TENDENCIES IN ESTIMATES OF BODY BUILD AND
TEMPERAMENT FOR 151 OFFICE WORKERS, MEN AND WOMEN

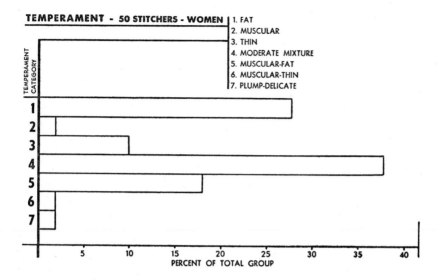

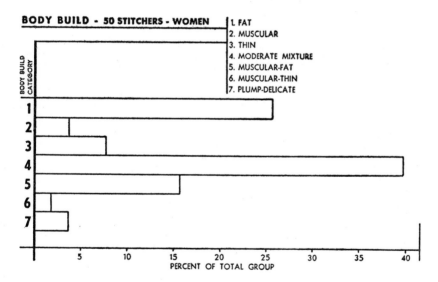

Fig. 11 — COMPARATIVE TENDENCIES IN ESTIMATES OF BODY BUILD AND
TEMPERAMENT FOR 50 STITCHERS, WOMEN

She said to me, "What would I say?" The other feminine THIN held her breath while she did a little test we shall come to soon— called the Dot Test. None of the other subjects did this. She didn't have gagging spells like the extreme THIN, but her breathing had a way of stopping. I think these instances clarify the difference between an extreme example of a type (even what may be considered a "stressed" extreme) and what I have called a "sport"—a type which shows inappropriate behavior for his major tendencies.

I think we feel well enough acquainted with our "sample" people and even with our "sample of a deviant" to interpret quickly for ourselves their behavior on the few remaining tests. We have "met" everybody now.

Relaxation and Praise

On Table 16 (Sigh Data), we noticed that all subjects sighed *less* or *not at all* when they were relaxed. And when they were praised, there was only one sigh by one person (PLUMP-DELICATE) out of all who took the test. (THIN and MUSCULAR-FAT m. didn't take the test.) Even the FAT-MUSCULAR "sport" didn't sigh once on the "praise" run. He needed this reassurance and responded to it. He might have said truthfully, "I can 'breathe easier' now." And THIN's *relaxation* run was the least sighing of any except his routine "learning" and "vital capacity" run. He benefited from relaxation as compared to his other test situations.

Our pronounced MUSCULARS had left before these tests. However, during the course of the tests they took, it was noticeable that strong, assured, MUSCULAR subjects neither responded particularly well to *praise* nor even liked it. They had confidence in themselves and didn't *need* praise.

On the other hand, they didn't react poorly to criticism. It made them determined to overcome the "weak spot" that was criticized. We used scoring on the Dot Test for some of these checks. I think the findings will be of more interest than the mechanics of the test situation. A higher score meant better performance on the test. After criticism, MUSCULARS would resume the test with renewed determination. THINS and PLUMP-DELICATES would "crack up" under criticism and their scores would "go to pieces."

Startle

One breathing test had the clash of a cymbal during the run (Startle). To provide data for scoring, the Dot Test was used with this run before and after the breathing. Table 16 (Sigh Data) and Table 18 show the sigh and pertinent Dot scoring data.

Most striking results were those of MUSCULAR-FAT f. and of PLUMP-DELICATE. MUSCULAR-FAT didn't sigh at all. When I exclaimed over it after the test, she said smoothly she didn't mind

TABLE 18

DIFFERENCES IN
DOT TEST SCORES AFTER STARTLE

	LESS REACTIVE	MORE REACTIVE
PLUMP-DELICATE f.		—60 (drop)
MUSCULAR-FAT f.	—2 (drop)	
MODERATE MIXTURE f.	+27 (raise)	

things like that. Once she had to have a wart taken off her foot, she said. The doctor put ether on the skin before he began. Somehow it caught on fire. She looked down and saw her foot on fire. "Everybody got so excited!" she said. "I guess other people mind those things more than the person does himself. I didn't mind."

At the other end of the series, PLUMP-DELICATE *jumped out of he machine* when the cymbal clashed! The oxygen tube came out of her mouth.

As you will see in Table 18, her Dot Test after the run had sixty more errors than the one she did before the run. By contrast MUSCULAR-FAT's was only two points poorer. MODERATE MIXTURE f., who had one sigh on the part of the breathing test following the clash, *improved* by twenty-seven points over her pretest Dot run. In other words, MUSCULAR-FAT f. and MODERATE MIXTURE f. came through with flying colors. PLUMP-DELICATE "folded"!

Hooton's remarks in *Young Man, You Are Normal* about the "resting" (basal metabolism) breathing patterns taken in connection with the Harvard Grant Study subjects (209 college men) have a familiar ring:

So, there may be discerned at one end of the scale four groups of respiratory imperturbables (bland effect, humanistic, practical organizing and pragmatic) who remind me of a hymn we used to sing in Sunday school:

> *Not a sigh nor a tear,*
> *Not a doubt nor a fear*
> *Can abide if we trust and obey.*

I gather that these fellows trust themselves and obey conventions. At the other end are the doubters, the aesthetes, the idealists, the thin-skinned, and the disorganized (self-conscious, introspective, lack of purpose, cultural, asocial, ideational, inhibited, shy, unstable autonomic, sensitive affect, less well-integrated). . . . I am especially intrigued by the less well-integrated, who seem to be practically rent asunder with sighs (7 per cent, no sighs; 45 per cent, excessive sighers).[10]

It is of interest that we have one certainly "less well-integrated" FAT-*MUSCULAR* sigher and one stressed, extreme THIN sigher. If the trends of our few tests had gone in a contrary direction from the findings referred to here, we might hesitate even to mention such a small series. But when these straws are being blown in the same direction as other people's findings, they take on scientific respectability and, so far as we are concerned, "make sense" in the light of what we know of our chosen subjects.

---

[10]We may recall that "excessive" sighers have been defined as those who sigh three times in two minutes or more frequently.

18. How Are Your Brain Waves Waving?
Is Your Heart on the Downbeat?
and
How Tense CAN You Get?

AND, OF COURSE, WE CANNOT OVERLOOK the fact that, while some people may sigh or stammer, others under the same amount of stress may have indigestion or a rapid or palpitating pulse. Naturally, there are also other alternatives.

To investigate a few, we took subjects from our series to the Brain Wave laboratory at the Massachusetts General Hospital in Boston. These were some of our last tests and a number of subjects had left us by this time. Of the people we know, however, we are lucky to have MUSCULAR-FAT m. and THIN m., as well as the MODERATE MIXTURE—MUSCULAR m. If we can understand what a few subjects did and how their performances compared, in the light of all we know about them already, we may be able to track down a few more "straws in the wind."

Three kinds of tests were used. The two in addition to the Brain Wave were: measurement of heart rate (E.K.G.—electrocardiogram) and an electrical test which measured the amount of electricity in a muscle, called a "myogram," E.M.G. The myogram reflected the tension in a muscle. We must remember that these three tests

(Figures 12-14) were the most "exploratory" of all! Consequently, only a few comments seem justified at this time.

EFFECT OF MUSIC AND NOISE ON THE BRAIN WAVE

Considering what we know about MUSCULAR people's enthusiasm for marches, we may not be surprised to notice (Figures 12-13) that the "quick" brain waves (called "alpha" and coming eight to thirteen per second) increased in both the back (occipital) and side (parietal) parts of the brain wave recording for both MUSCULAR-FAT m. and pronounced MUSCULAR m. when they heard a march playing.

MUSCULAR-FAT got a few more "fast" waves with the noise following the march. However, MUSCULAR disdained to react to noise and returned to his original rate in the "back" (occipital) region; the "sides" (parietals) of his head showed even fewer fast waves than before the march.

The slow waves—which are more frequent in sleep—tend to appear in opposite tendencies from the fast as is to be expected. In other words, less total "sleepy"—slow—waves appeared during the march for both MUSCULAR-FAT and MUSCULAR. With noise, MUSCULAR-FAT had the same number for the back of his head as he had during the

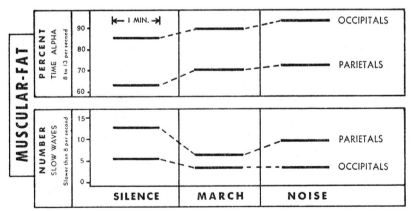

Fig. 12 — EFFECT OF MUSIC AND NOISE ON THE BRAIN WAVE
(Adapted from a chart made at E.E.G. Laboratory, Massachusetts
General Hospital)

march and only a few more for the sides. However, MUSCULAR shows up with *many more slow waves for noise* than for the march. (The noise recording was the one used on the Fatigue Lab tests.)

Whether this reflects "disdain" for noise or is a "draggy" effect of the irritating sound might be argued. The only fact which we can boldly assert is that MUSCULAR-FAT and MUSCULAR do *not* react *alike*. There are differences. We would like to know more about what these differences mean.

EFFECT OF MUSIC AND NOISE
ON MUSCLE TENSION AND HEARTRATE
(while working [Dot Test] and at rest)

As usual, MUSCULAR-FAT and THIN, whom we have followed through a number of tests now, give us striking contrasts in performance and reaction. In Figure 14, we are struck by the fact that MUSCULAR-FAT's large muscle—whether tense or relaxed—has more potential energy (as shown in microvolts) *all* through the test than THIN's small,

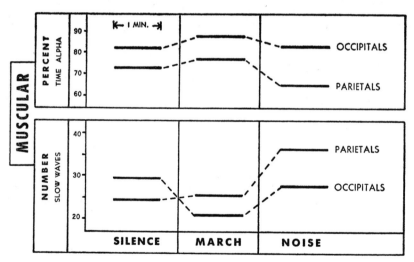

Fig. 13 — EFFECT OF MUSIC AND NOISE ON THE BRAIN WAVE
(Adapted from a chart made at E.E.G. Laboratory, Massachusetts
General Hospital)

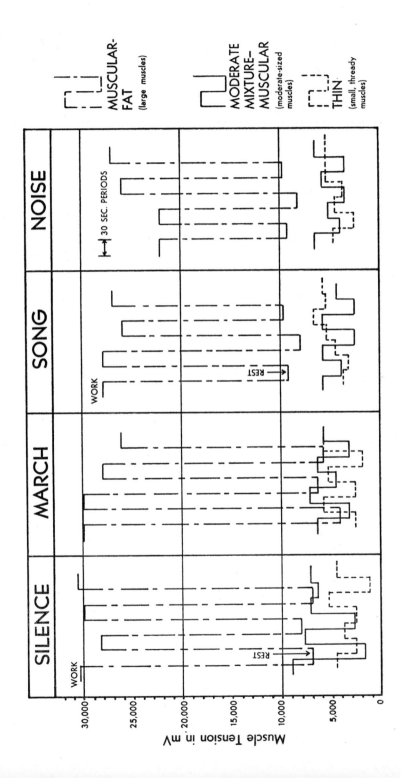

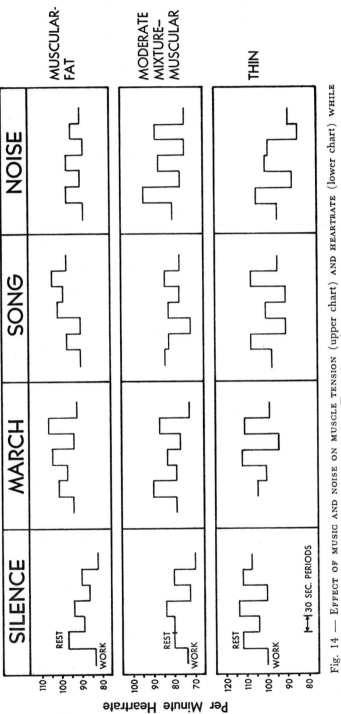

Fig. 14 — EFFECT OF MUSIC AND NOISE ON MUSCLE TENSION (upper chart) AND HEARTRATE (lower chart) WHILE DOING THE DOT TEST (WORK) AND RESTING

(Adapted from charts made at E.E.G. Laboratory, Massachusetts General Hospital)

thready muscle has at *any* time during the test. Muscular-fat shows a logical variation in level of output for work or rest. His tension readings show a deep, regular reaction. Naturally, his muscle is tense while he uses it and then it relaxes when he is not working. Thin, on the other hand, starts out in a rather "regular" fashion; maintains this with slightly greater regularity when the march plays; but the sentimental song, "I'll Be Seeing You" crooned by Bing Crosby, puts him out of phase. His muscle does not tense and relax regularly in relation to the test activity. His tension mounts. Noise makes him less tense, but not regular.

Meanwhile, muscular-fat has reacted along throughout march, song, and noise with very little change. He too is a bit less tense on noise.

You can see from Figure 14 that moderate mixture—muscular is a bit tense at the start, but soon "gets his stride" and rides through the test regularly and—with his moderate-sized muscle—approximately between big, strong muscular-fat and small, delicate thin.

While these tests reflect the amount of tension in a muscle of the forearm (flexor) when doing the Dot Test or when *not* doing it, the "picture" which results on the chart is not too far from the appearance of breathing patterns for the three types. Muscular-fat is a deep, regular performer. Thin is a relatively shallower and definitely more erratic performer. Moderate mixture (with muscular emphasis here) is a middle range, fairly consistent reactor.

One thing, however, did show up on almost all the heartrate (Dot Test) records which we ran. As you will notice on the three records (Figure 14), the "resting" heartrate is higher than the "working" rate.

The Dot Test required attention but was not "heavy" work. For problems of nervous fatigue with resultant "tension," this poses some interesting problems.

Now let's see how hearts are beating during march, sentimental song, or noise. Look at the heartrate line for each of the three subjects. Heartrate for both muscular-fat and moderate mixture —muscular show noticeable rises during the playing of the march.

However, neither of them show more tension in the myogram record above, nor do they become erratic. It looks as though they "felt peppier," but in a way which didn't make them tense and "under pressure." In other words, they "liked" marches in their physiology. This agrees with what they had told us, and it also bears out the popularity of marches for "pick-ups" and "pepper-uppers"—whether an office worker beginning the day, whether a marching soldier or a weary worker on a heavy, physical job.

Even THIN didn't get "upset" by the march. In fact, his tension "work" rhythm was most even of any of the four periods of the test. His heartrate was not significantly raised. Nor did the sentimental song affect his heart except in a regulatory way. His breathing may go "haywire" but his heart is a better behaved organ.

Therefore, we see the sentimental song upset THIN's tension and relaxation, raised MUSCULAR-FAT's heartrate by increments which are not very different from his reaction to the march. By contrast, however, MODERATE MIXTURE—MUSCULAR was *not* stimulated by the crooning and falls back to more nearly his original heart pattern. In terms of what we know of MUSCULAR-FAT personality trends, it appears that he has some MUSCULAR reaction here (to the march), but also some sentimental FAT reaction to the soft song.

Noise, on the other hand, neither stimulates nor seriously depresses MUSCULAR-FAT's heart nor does it make him tense. MODERATE MIXTURE—MUSCULAR rises to the irritant, however; his heart hits a new high; but be sure to notice it does not make him tense as manifested in his "work" tension above. He can "take it" from a work point of view, even if it does annoy him. We recall that MUSCULARS on the targetometer said they didn't "mind" noise or talking. By contrast, THIN has no rising heartrate with noise, but he suffers a little heart irregularity and his "work" tension becomes erratic, with final inability to remain in any state but perpetual tension.

I think you will agree with me that, however "exploratory" these tests are, these are *the people we know.*

Part V -

C
O
M
P   OFFICE
A
R
I
S
O
N
S

FACTORY

LABORATORY

ARMY

COMPARISONS

Weighed in the Balance

or

Tipping the Scales

WHETHER WE KNOW IT OR NOT, we've all been waiting with Textron until "all the facts could be weighed together." This was the "long-range plan" we talked about back on page 85. As we are only too well aware, we have been concentrating our attention on body build and behavior, on nervous strain and fatigue. When these factors are put into the scales *with everything else,* we want to know what will tip the scales.

We cannot bob up with a panacea. Every situation has slightly different angles. We can only discuss what we have experienced. We can only mention the straws we have seen blowing in the wind. This can be done very briefly, as we've all seen them together. First, let's list some of the things that seemed to please or bother *everybody.* Then we'll simply bring to mind those that appeared to be especially pleasing or especially difficult for certain types of people.

161

19. ALL WORKERS...

Work which was "boring" bored everyone—in the office or in the factory or in the lab! (Filetab, p. 35; Textron, p. 63; targetometer subjects.) Stoic musculars could "stand it" best.

Workers of all builds in office and factory and subjects running the targetometer in the lab had to contend with the eyestrain inherent in the job. In the office, this was particularly acute for the comptometer workers (p. 40). In the factory, while general lighting was good, the vibrating light on the machine and glare from satin and other reflection didn't help (p. 64). In the lab, tests were not sufficiently long to cause drastic complaints but subjects commented on eye fatigue—particularly at first. As might be expected THIN was fairly vehement in his comment. He said, "It's hell on the eyes." Supervisors in the factory felt that workers who were particularly unhappy or maladjusted for various reasons were apt to complain *more* about the eyestrain.

Everyone liked the "nice" supervisors who were fair and knew the job. Remember Lorna at Filetab and Jeanie at Textron (Filetab,

162

p. 32; Textron, pp. 75, 95, and 104)? A few high-producing veterans liked "drivers" for supervisors, according to the Textron manager (p. 83).

Both office workers and stitchers liked to know what their work "goal" was. Filetab workers liked to know when there was a particular "deadline" to meet (Filetab, p. 49). "If they'd just tell you *how many!*" said MUSCULAR-FAT ("number eight") at Textron (p. 102).

Any worker would be apt to resent *being transferred "back"*— being *demoted!* (p. 78, Textron). We recall the Filetab policy of a regular, carefully-worked-out sequence of jobs beginning with Transfer (p. 37).

Everyone minded having to "wait in line" at Textron (p. 62) with a short lunch period. At Filetab the line moved quickly and the 45-minute lunch period made no rush with eating. *All* workers benefited from this.

Bobby-soxers at both office and factory were "famous" for their chatter and the added noise and confusion they made. In the factory the vibration of machines increased the impact of their arrival (pp. 63-64, and 71).

All workers in both places appreciated having an attractive "lounge" (Filetab) or "smoking room" (Textron *after* the redecorating). However, it was used much more by some workers than by others. FAT social and "relaxable" leanings made them naturals for a "lounge." Some of the more ambitious or compulsive workers needed to be encouraged to "take a break" more often.

Restful green-and-cream color schemes delighted all workers whether in factory or office.

And it seemed to me a pleasant outdoor "view" would be enjoyed by most everyone. You remember how I liked it in Transfer, missed it in Comps (p. 40), and mentioned the problem at Textron (pp. 68-69). How about a factory patio or garden where possible? Either as a view or also for rest periods in nice weather. It could even be a "penthouse" garden in a crowded city!

Most people responded favorably to plants.

There was also an enthusiastic response to the rotating art exhibits in the Smoking Room at Textron. Only one rather negative person was indifferent in her attitude. A number of workers who were not in the habit of using the Smoking Room liked the idea of having pictures, noticed new ones as they were put in, and missed the pictures the period when we left the wall vacant. Other workers who had not been in the habit of using the Smoking Room began to do so. —In general, comments of workers suggested that, for a number of them at least, the changing pictures made a pleasant diversion, "took up their mind," made an enjoyable break from the job and provided a chance to relax in a "home-like" atmosphere.

With only one or two notable exceptions, everyone at Filetab and Textron *liked* having music. While everyone liked music, it did interfere with some types of work—as we saw at Filetab. When this was the case, workers enjoyed music during the lunch hour or at the start and end of the day. Now we come to the problem of *differences*.

20. DIFFERENCES

In looking back over the varied reactions to music throughout our program of research, I was more convinced than ever that no piece could be arbitrarily labelled "excellent" or "good" (p. 46). Take marches, for instance. Our laboratory tests indicated that they were stimulating and particularly enjoyed by MUSCULARS. Of the seven MUSCULAR women in the office, five *did* like them. However, most office workers found marches *too* stimulating for their type of sedentary work. It made them feel "like getting up and going somewhere." Played first thing in the morning to wake them up or last thing at night as they were "getting up to leave" was acceptable.

From the office reactions, one might assume that marches were too stimulating for sedentary workers. Factory workers, however, were very enthusiastic about marches. I felt the effect and wrote, "They seemed to steady me as I did the stitching. . . it went more evenly and faster." Stitching was a more active, less "intellectual" job than office work.

Offhand, I would have predicted that the young male MUSCULARS doing the active, nonsedentary Collating would have been "naturals" for marches. However, they felt marches were too "set" and even "slow" for their work. They wanted lively dance music, you may recall (p. 47). And I added, "Even jive might be all right for Collating although, I was told, it made the sedentary bobby-soxers jump around in their seats" (p. 47).

When we look back and see the effects on brain waves (Figures 12 and 13), on heartrate and muscle tension (Figure 14), we realize that when you add a stimulant to a situation, it is important to know who is being stimulated, what he is doing, and whether a stimulant will *agree* with him and his job.

In determining what music is "good" or "excellent," we need to ask many questions. Does this worker need to be stimulated? Does he need to be soothed and relaxed? Or does he simply need a variety of pieces as distraction from his boredom? Does he know and like this kind of music—is it familiar without having been "killed" by too frequent repetition? Does it suit his work rhythm?

The few clues we have noted in this research show us what important uses can be made of sound—and also of color—for producing predictable effects in known situations. We have glimpsed some of the good and bad effects. Noise reactions, for instance, were more detrimental to some people than to others. Musculars and muscular-fats appeared to mind it least. Of course, we were not working in high decibels where there was actually question of possible physiological damage.

As to talking, the problem has been pretty well covered by muscular-fat ("number eight," p. 103). The fact that types tend to be talkers—like sociable fats—or quiet—like strong, silent musculars or mature, inhibited thins—should help in some general points. The fact that thins are easily distracted, especially from a boring job, heightens their talkativeness in this situation. However, compulsive thin workers will not be tempted. Naturally, the better a supervisor knows his workers, the better he can place them in relation to their neighbors.

We recall the different effects on the lab subjects (pp. 126-127,

129). We know some people, like MUSCULAR, can perform at their usual rate and carry on a lively conversation. We know it "shot" MUSCULAR-*THIN*'s performance. As MUSCULAR-FAT suggests, a conscientious person knows whether it is ruining his output. We saw how workers at Filetab—as those on Comps—didn't talk because they couldn't and "put out the work."

While job changes and problems of "making the quote" bothered most of the stitchers, MUSCULAR-FATS made fewest complaints and THINS (including PLUMP-DELICATES) took it hardest (p. 91). It seemed to me, after hearing comments and picking up the trends of complaints, that "making the quote" was not as much a problem of doing the job itself as it was of "interferences." Even with some allowance for these, changes, repairs, and machine trouble made "making the quote" virtually impossible much of the time for all but the top performers.

FATS appeared to let the strain "slide off" them whereas THINS got all "nerved up." No MUSCULAR-FAT appeared tense during my interviews with stitchers. The whole picture brought to mind the contrast we've just seen in the lab when MUSCULAR-FAT calmly told about not "minding" her foot's being on fire!—and PLUMP-DELICATE jumped out of the machine at the clash of a cymbal!

With what we know of the office and stitching jobs, we can now begin to see why we found *fewer* THINS *in the factory*. Both physically and nervously, the stitcher's job put more strain on THINS than did the office jobs. And how about the other distributions of workers we looked at in Part I? Do they "make sense" in the light of what we know now?

21. A BIRD'S-EYE VIEW

LET'S GLANCE AGAIN AT THOSE ASSORTMENTS WE SAW at the beginning of the book. How did the types cluster in the army groups as compared with totals for office and factory? To give us a quick flash-back, I've made Table 11 (p. 23) into five "pies" (Figure 15). Looking at the "pies," we see that they are sliced differently. Each slice represents the per cent of that type found in the group.

The thing that jumped out at me when I first looked at the five "pies" was the fact that approximately one-half of the WAC Officers "pie" was made up of MUSCULARS, MUSCULAR-THINS, and THINS. By comparison, the small part of the factory "pie" occupied by these types was a joke.

But it's just as funny to compare the tiny "pieces" of FAT and MUSCULAR-FAT in the WAC Officers "pie" with the enormous portions for factory workers. Of course, we've been noticing that MUSCULAR-FATS were the "best bets" of the factory. In relation to nervous strain, we have lauded FAT calm as a feature of both FATS and MUSCULAR-FATS. But that was looking at the stresses of stitching and at who could do it best and stand it best. Other jobs might

168

well show other types—just the types who were disadvantaged at
the machine—as favorites. And now here they are. These two "pies"
tell us that jobs can be so different in their requirements that you
may find different assortments of people doing them.

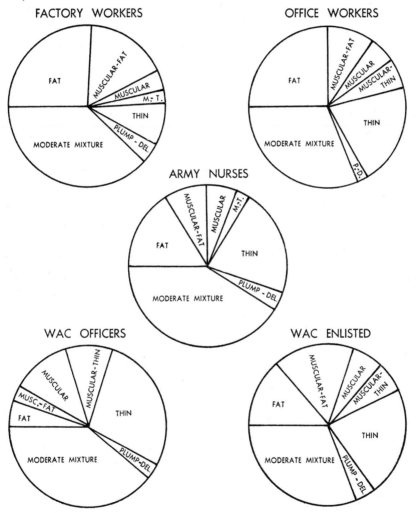

Fig. 15 — A NEW LOOK AT SOME OF THE GROUPS WE MET IN THE FIRST PART
OF THE BOOK

Though assortments differ, all five "pies" have a large number of MODERATE MIXTURES. It looks as though they can fit in most anywhere and survive. They can veer in the most directions. But "top" performers in some spots may be people with one or two pronounced trends. We need to know more about which occupations have these specialized requirements.

While I collected no data on WAC Officers' performance or job requirements, much work has been done on the selection of male officer candidates. Countless studies of this are reported in journals and monographs. While none exactly suits our needs, we can glean some hints from these researches. The terminology or emphasis of the report may be different from the present study, but the implications are very clear.

Officer candidates are usually chosen from people who have more than a high school education. They are most often college trained. The assumption is that the job requires intellectual capacity. On the other hand, officers must have sufficient self-assertion and aggression to take a position of leadership. Initiative and forcefulness are key requirements for many tasks assigned to male officers. Male officers also need strength and physical endurance. In all, laziness, inefficiency, and slow reactions may be costly in terms of men and material.

Leadership may be most harmonious where understanding and sympathy with people is combined with other traits—as has been found out for successful store executives. However, army authority is based on "orders" which "have" to be followed rather than primarily on loyalty. The business executive may offend his employees at his peril. They can leave. The army officer does not have to have consummate tact to keep his personnel! Apparently, FAT traits are not essential for "dealing with people" in the army situation.

For these reasons, as we look at the constellation of traits which go with MUSCULARS (Figures 5, 6, and pp. 123-124), we find the requisite self-assertion, aggression, and courage. THIN traits show trends to intellectual interest. The fact that FAT traits tend to be "soft," "sociable," and—when extreme—"lazy" may account for their low incidence among the officers, whereas they can fit into a sedentary job. As the factory FAT said, " I *love* to sit."

The army had found our extreme THIN a psychological 4F; there were few—if any—unmixed THINS in the army sample. It should be mentioned that army policy, in general, was to screen out extreme over- or underweights.

In some instances, special experience or training or unusually high motivation may overcome the drawback of a less favored body type for a particular job. Also, we need to know whether there are a few "atypical" jobs within the occupation itself which can use—or even need—people of the "unfavored" type.

In general, however, it looks as though MUSCULAR and THIN qualities were required for the duties of WAC Officers whereas FAT traits were a liability. It looks as though MUSCULAR and FAT qualities were required for the job of stitching and as though THIN traits were liabilities. In other words, we have here only a few occupations, but they can serve as "straws in the wind" to tell us that *some jobs appear to require special types of people and appear to find other types unsuitable.* Our research has only begun. We need to know more about *which occupations* require *which assortments* of people.

If jobs can accommodate an average assortment or if there is a slight "skewing" in some direction, that is good to know too. The selection requirements won't have to be as "tough." Anyone can have an equal chance at the job. Placing within the occupation itself may easily become the major concern.

Let's look at the other three "pies." The Army nurses fall nearest the average distribution for the total 727 women. One point, however, should be made here. Comparisons between the three army groups alone (WAC Officers, WAC Enlisted, and Army Nurses) place Army Nurses far ahead of WAC Officers in FAT women and a bit ahead of WAC Enlisted. However, compared with civilian factory and civilian office workers, they have decidedly *less* FAT women. Therefore, of these five groups, sedentary factory and office workers have more FATS than any of the three army groups (WAC Officer or Enlisted, or Army Nurse).

Much more needs to be known of the nurse group and their particular activities to interpret the placing of the various types and their reactions to their jobs. At present we must satisfy ourselves with distributions and their tendencies. We can see whether the five "pies" we have and the comparative distributions made by others "make sense."

Dr. R. W. Parnell, Research Physician in the Constitutional Aspects of Psychiatric Medicine, The Warneford Hospital, Oxford, England, was formerly Student Health Physician at the Institute of Social Medicine at Oxford University. For five years he studied Oxford students and has recently (June, 1954) published an article on "The Current and Subsequent Health of Athletes."[11] I think you will be interested in some of his comments on occupational trends in distribution. I shall quote his remarks but substitute "ordinary" words for the longer terms he uses (such substitutions are italicized). In discussing body type and occupational health, he writes:

Fitness for this or that occupation is related to physique. A *body-type* study . . . of choice of faculty at the university shows doctors, dentists and mechanical engineers as most frequently *extreme MUSCULARS,* and to this the later observation may be added that metallurgists were even more *MUSCULAR* "men of steel." Chelsea Pensioners, some of whom had survived the hardships of three wars and many years' military service, were strongly *MUSCULAR* although often too short of stature to have competed successfully in field sports. Miners, farm labourers, and heavy manual workers no doubt number a large proportion of *MUSCULARS* in their midst; clerks [this is used to designate clerical office workers in England], shop assistants and others in sedentary work show less. It is, of course, possible to influence the relative proportion of fat and muscle development by feeding and exercise, but the change in measurements

[11]*The Medical Press,* ccxxxi, 6007 (June 23, 1954).

so introduced in healthy persons seldom results in more than one unit difference in estimates. . . . Thus environmental changes seem small compared with the constitutional range encountered, though it cannot be denied that small as they are, they may influence the development or otherwise of illness.

Dr. Parnell's comments on trends in sedentary jobs is of interest. Also, his last statement as to the effect of even *slight* change in trends of a body build is important. We have seen how much difference it made in the factory when we were dealing with an "extreme" THIN or with one who had "some" MUSCULAR or FAT *and* MUSCULAR support. A PLUMP-DELICATE was too devoid of MUSCULAR strength, but a THIN with some MUSCULAR or combined FAT and MUSCULAR could "take" a lot of things that would make an extreme THIN "go to pieces" or a PLUMP-DELICATE "jump out of the machine."

Also some of the FAT drawbacks may be alleviated by "reducing." Parnell points this out in relation to health problems of the middle-aged person. However, as he wisely comments at the end of his article, "In eschewing food. . . may they not lose their warmth and human touch."

We must not forget that each tendency has its advantages and disadvantages, its assets and liabilities. Excess of any tendency is more apt to bring some traits into exaggerated form without the offsetting influence of other trends. If we find ourselves an extreme THIN, we may want to try to move "even slightly" in one or both of the other directions, may benefit from both a little added weight and muscular development.

A pure MUSCULAR may want a little FAT softening to smooth some of his social relationships. Whereas a PLUMP-DELICATE needs to develop muscular strength and confidence enough in the self to offset timidity and show constructive self-assertion. If MUSCULAR traits of even microscopic amount are developed in a PLUMP-DELICATE, life may not look so frightening. A pronounced FAT may want to move in THIN directions, or after THIN enough, add a little more activity and MUSCULAR tone to his make-up.

When it comes to our reactions to nervous strain, these little changes may mean just the difference between outburst or calm, between collapse or survival. There are ways to help ourselves. As we learn more about our own tendencies, we can make slight alterations, if need be; and find the most auspicious spot in life for our particular talents.

INDEX